S0-ACD-441

From prehistoric cave art to abstract expressionism, from the Orient to the Western world —the six volumes in this series provide a panoramic view of man's achievements and his aspirations as they have been expressed in painting. The illustrations, all in full color, have been chosen with an eye to their freshness as well as their intrinsic worth: many of these masterpieces are virtually inaccessible to even the most dedicated art lover. Each volume is introduced by a leading authority in the field, who presents his insights in lucid, simple prose. Hans L. C. Jaffé, Professor of Modern Art at the University of Amsterdam, has edited the series with knowledge and care, to make *20,000 Years of World Painting* both a major esthetic experience and an exciting introduction to the history of art. The volumes in the series are:

H. HETL-KUNTZE

Far
Eastern
Art

EDITED BY *Hans L. C. Jaffé*
TRANSLATED BY *Robert Erich Wolf*

20,000 Years of World Painting

VOLUME VI

Published by
DELL PUBLISHING CO., INC.
750 Third Avenue
New York, New York 10017

Copyright 1967 by Smeets Lithographers, Weert, Holland

Laurel ® TM 674623, Dell Publishing Co., Inc.

Originally published as part of one volume
entitled 20,000 YEARS OF WORLD PAINTING

Reprinted by arrangement with
Harry N. Abrams, Incorporated

Manufactured in the Netherlands

First printing—1968

INTRODUCTION

This survey of painting of the Far East is designed to give some idea of the rich diversity of artistic creation in that part of the world. In a development spanning more than two thousand years, not all of which has even yet been thoroughly studied, it provides us with innumerable examples that demonstrate the relationship of the Far East to the art of color—color so much the more interesting for having its own unique and characteristic traits.

All painting depends on color, however restrictive that definition may seem. Even in grisaille—the monochromatic painting often used for frescoes or stained glass—the gradations of a single color inevitably suggest coloristic effects. This makes all the more understandable the Oriental insistence that India ink, with its all-inclusive range from palest gray to deepest black, contains within itself all the colors of the world. India-ink painting is one of the chief glories of Far Eastern art, and it was at the very moment when the range of vision of the West first began to conceive the world in impressionistic terms, with a new concern for light and atmosphere, that India-ink painting made its most universal impact. Today, in the perspective of time, that impact seems so immense that no one can any longer ignore or deprecate Oriental art.

But instead of coming to grips on its own terms with this still little-known but, for all that, no less interesting medium of Far Eastern art, the West has tended to imitate its aesthetic effects while employing a range of colors entirely alien to its basic character. Those of us who love India-ink painting find that it loses its significance when transposed into color. The tonal values are all too often debased and often enough quite simply falsified. Any color juxtaposed to ink distorts: the cinnabar red of certain wax seals stamped on pictures in the Orient to indicate ownership creates such an intense color contrast that often the total impression of the picture is disturbed. (Unfortunately, Emperor Ch'ien-lung was not alone in his mania of so marking every picture in his collection.) However, we need not limit ourselves to such a special case to see just how important and objective a role color plays in Oriental painting.

5

Even a comparatively modest example of early Chinese art, the fragment of a lute dating from the fourth century B.C. (page 18), is characterized not only by the animated rhythms of its figures in silhouette but also by a secure instinct for the use of a few related colors. The twisting contours of the figures are typical of the style of the time, though they were exploited most fully in jade and bronze. As for the painting of that early era, we know something about it from the poems of Ch'u-yuan (c. 300 B.C.) which describe the wall paintings in the ruined palaces of his native state of Ch'u in Central China. The paintings on the walls of those wooden palaces have not come down to us, but their subject matter is known not only from Ch'u-yuan's poems but also from later versions of the same themes found in tomb chambers of the Han period (206 B.C. to A.D. 220).

It is to that period, the first century or the beginning of the second of our era, that the lacquer painting on the lidded pannier unearthed at Lo-Lang in northern Korea belongs (page 19). Northern Korea was a Chinese colony at that time, and most of the inscriptions incised on the bottoms of lacquered objects indicate the imperial workshops in Szechwan as their place of fabrication. The figures on the pannier lid, illustrating the subject of filial piety, are painted with a wealth of detail inside the contours, with finely harmonized colors, and with animated expression. Such art makes us regret so much the more the loss of all large-scale paintings.

The situation is no better for the next few centuries. For any idea of Chinese painting we still must depend on examples from provincial regions, such as the frescoes in tombs and cave temples from the outer borders of the vast empire. Yet, we do know something at least about the great artists of the time and the works they made to adorn palaces and temples, because they are spoken of in literary sources which, in China more than elsewhere, have survived in great numbers and from very early times. Even from the T'ang Dynasty (618–906), one of the truly brilliant periods of Chinese art and culture, scarcely a single noteworthy work of fine art, as distinguished from applied art, has survived through the ages, though it was precisely this epoch that had such great influence on the art of Japan.

Nara, the first stable capital of Japan, was patterned after Ch'ang-an, the capital of the T'ang Dynasty, and the same city served as the model for Kyoto which was founded in 794 and remained the chief city of Japan right up to 1868. In those Japanese centers, Chinese objects were used, some of which were imported, others turned out by native artists in strict imitation of Chinese proto-types. That is why, today, we often find it difficult to identify objects from the Shosoin, the treasure house founded in 756 in honor of Buddha by the widow of Emperor Shomu, which contained the entire domestic furnishings of the imperial household. Thanks to dedicated care through the centuries, its rich collections have survived to our time. Even though the most recent research has decided that most of the objects were Japanese in origin, these collections give us the best idea possible under the circumstances of what Chinese work of the same period was like, and with some justification we can disregard the question of precisely where the objects were, in fact, made.

The rich repertory of subject matter of the time—Buddhist scenes like that on the Tamamushi shrine (page 24), landscapes (page 25), and figures (page 28)—would never again appear simultaneously to such an extent. After the persecution of Buddhism in 843–45, when among other artworks the frescoes of Wu Tao-tzu (c. 690–760), unique in their kind, were destroyed, religious art using many figures disappeared almost entirely from China. It was supplanted, in the Sung period especially, by the restrained India-ink painting of the meditative form of Buddhism called Ch'an in China and in Japan, Zen. The outstanding examples of that art were often done by monks and were Japanese in origin. The Chinese themselves did not accord such great significance to this kind of painting, and in contemporary accounts there is little or no mention of the artists who made it. Be that as it may, in the classification of Emperor Hui-tsung's collection, Taoist and Buddhist themes take first place, even though they are outnumbered by pictures of flowers and birds. Hui-tsung was himself an excellent painter of such themes, as we can see in the small leaf from an album with a quail and narcissus (page 32). With Hui-tsung and the Southern Sung Academy, the decisive factor in landscape painting, as in that of flowers and birds, was asymmetrical composition in which the principal subject was placed not in the center but in a corner of the picture. This formal peculiarity, however, was less frequent in pictures on domestic themes and in those done for hand scrolls. Compare, for instance, Su Han-ch'en's *Children Playing* (page 38) or the anonymous *Homecoming of Wen-chi* (page 39) with Hui-tsung's *Quail and Narcissus* (page 32) or Li Ti's *Herdsman Returning Home* (page 36). In the former, the entire scenes are depicted in detail, in the latter there is only an intimation of the essential inner meaning. The distinction is summed up in a saying of Confucius: "I point out one corner, and for the man who cannot find the other three I will not repeat myself."

Beginning with the Southern Sung period, landscape became one of the chief subjects of Chinese painting; thenceforth no painter could ignore it. Even the greatest artists of the Yuan period, those who carried on the ideals of the Sung Academy, did their best work in landscapes which, as a part of the whole of nature, became a symbol of the free man. After the passing of the Mongols who had ruled China as the Yuan Dynasty, the native Chinese house of Ming acceded to the throne in 1368. It was at the court of Peking especially that the effort was made to pick up where the Sung Academy had been forced to leave off. This, then, became a time for the restoration of old values, and it was painters like Tai Wen-chin and Lu Chi (page 43) who rose to fame then. The former specialized in India-ink landscapes in the style of the Southern Sung Academy, the latter in birds and flowers. Had he lived under the Sung Dynasty, Lu Chi's carefully observed and naturalistic birds would have earned him great honor at the court of Hui-tsung, but his gleaming colors have much more in common with the decorative fashions of his own time.

Alongside this academic circle there was another and brilliant group of utmost importance: the so-called Four Great Painters of the Ming Dynasty—Shen Chou (page 46), Wen Cheng-ming (page 51), T'ang Yin (page 52), and Ch'iu Ying (page 50). These men merit as high a place in world art as their contemporaries Leonardo, Michelangelo, Grünewald, and Dürer. Although he passed all the state examinations with the highest distinction, Shen Chou declined to accept a post in Ho where attention was concentrated on the revival of the old styles. He lived apart from the world, though not averse to the company of friends, in his country place near Soochow in the old district of Wu. Forbidding as the towering mountain seems in his conception, his soft colors tone down the ruggedness of the place and the tiny figures he introduces lend a human dimension to an awesome landscape. Wen Cheng-ming, Shen Chou's friend and pupil, was subtler and more sensitive in both brushwork and color. For a short time he held an official post which only later, after many difficulties, he was able to secure definitively. Most of his life was spent as a free-lance teacher in Soochow where he wrote poetry, painted, and dedicated himself to literary studies. His brushwork is never bold and challenging like that of Shen Chou or the younger T'ang Yin, but rather has an unobtrusive delicacy and seems secondary to his interest in color. T'ang Yin's was the most unbridled personality of the group, and he painted not only landscapes but also remarkably fine figures. In the picture reproduced here, there is an enchanting still life of flowers in the foreground, and the rocks and landscape on the screen in the background are done in soft ink washes. In addition, the subtle, effective drawing of the figure and plum branch is skillfully combined with a restrained but fresh approach to color. Through intrigues, T'ang Yin never obtained an official post but, instead, passed his days in the company of beautiful women (it is said of him that he would paint a picture merely for a cup of wine). The youngest of the circle, Ch'iu Ying, was the only one not from a well-to-do family. Obliged to earn his daily bread by his art, it is a tribute to his native endowments that he is reckoned among the great artists of his country. His figures and landscapes are executed with delicate brushwork, though his colors tend to be vivid. Unfortunately, his works have been so often imitated and counterfeited that it is difficult to discern the qualities which his contemporaries admired in his pictures.

At the end of the sixteenth century appeared an artist whose overpowering personality set the tone for China's artistic life for a long time to come: Tung Ch'i-ch'ang (pages 54, 55). His brushwork is relatively easy to recognize: he is always concerned with exposing clearly the structure of a tree or crag and uses color only to emphasize the form and to intensify the effect of his ink drawing. The principles he laid down—the most significant of any of the old masters'—were followed more literally by his circle of friends and students than by the great painter himself, although many of his authentic works remain to be identified and may possibly contradict this. Not only was he painter, calligrapher, theorist, tutor to the prince, and minister, but he was also esteemed as one of the finest connoisseurs of painting: a work that he saw or an inscription he praised was and still is considered of greater value than any other. His high reputation and fame were due also, in part, to his friends and students. These included the four Wangs, Yun Shou-p'ing, and Wu Li who collectively are known as the Six Famous Masters of the Ch'ing Period. Contemporary with Tung Ch'i-ch'ang and his circle was the quite different school of Che, followers of the almost two-centuries-old tradition of Tai Wen-chin. They are represented here by two fresh and lively pictures by Li Shih-ta and Lan Ying (pages 58–60).

In the seventeenth century the Manchus overran the country and, as a sign of submission, ordered the Chinese to wear the pigtail. Many of the best and most independent spirits of the time turned their backs on the new rulers and withdrew from public life: they became monks and had their heads shorn so as not to have to wear the pigtail. Many of them entered monasteries, like Shih-ch'i and Hung-jen, while others, such as Shih-t'ao and Pa-ta-shan-jen, took to wandering about the country. The latter two were related to the imperial house of Ming (their official names were Chu Jo-ch'i and Chu Ta) and spent their later years in Yangchow where, upon occasion, they collaborated on the same work. In time, these four highly independent artists came to be known as the Individualists. The two pages from albums by Shih-t'ao seen here (pages 62, 63) use blue and red as intensifying colors. Considered the colors of the free spirit, blue and red were used first in landscapes of the Yuan period and are strikingly prominent in pictures by the Individualists.

Contemporary with these impassioned spirits, who felt themselves rejected and so chose voluntary exile, were the so-called Six Famous Masters of the Ch'ing Period (or, more precisely, of the seventeenth century) and they enjoyed the highest social standing. Wang Hui, one of the two younger of the four Wangs, is represented here by two characteristic landscapes (pages 64, 66); his younger friend Yun Shou-p'ing by a page from an album with a delicately sensitive branch of flowers (page 71). Yun Shou-p'ing's flower pictures are for the most part done entirely in color without any preliminary skeleton of ink. This "Western" technique was known and practiced in China as far back as the sixth century, as literary sources tell us, but no early examples have survived. It was not until the eighteenth century, however, that with the Emperor's support European influence actually made its impact felt, though commercial relations had begun in 1517 and through them European objects and books had been introduced into China. But there was no real effect on the upper strata of society until the arrival of the Jesuit missionaries, especially Castiglione who was awarded the post of privy councilor under his Chinese name of Lang Shih-ning (not the least part of his success was due to his proficiency in the Chinese language). Emperor Ch'ien-lung was interested in everything new and was ready for any experiment (unfortunately, not in painting alone). He had himself portrayed many times with his horse and attendants (page 72) and also required Castiglione to execute for him studies from nature of plants and birds. To Chinese eyes most of these works seemed uncouth, deficient in brush technique and so heavily shaded as to disturb the total impression. Nevertheless, the Emperor insisted that his court painters study under Lang Shih-ning and vice versa. What such docile students turned out can be seen in pictures by Wang Ch'eng-p'ei (page 76) and Tsou I-kuei (page 73). Tsou I-kuei's picture is at least plausible, what with the fine shading of ink, especially in the rocks, and the animated movement of the crane, but Wang Ch'eng-p'ei's shows what happened to a too impressionable student.

10 A number of important painters kept aloof from the academic

circle around Emperor Ch'ien-lung. Of these, the group called the Eight Fauves of Yangchow stands out for the unconstrained way they manipulate ink and for their highly witty compositions. Despite their name, these painters had only the vaguest ties with Yangchow—only Kao Hsiang was actually born there. They took up again the style of the Individualists but coarsened it in a somewhat humorous manner and without the passionate awareness of self so remarkable in their revered predecessors. Besides Kao Hsiang, the group is generally said to comprise Cheng Hsieh, Huang Shen, Li Fang-ying, Wang Shih-shen, Li Shan, Lo P'ing, and Chin Nung, and only the last-named is represented here, although with one of his best works. His *Lo-han* (page 78) shows better than words just what the Chinese mean by a "wild beast of a painter," what we call a Fauve. That these painters, in spite of their coarse brushwork (often they laid on paint with their fingers or a twist of paper), really knew how to wield the instrument is proved by the subtle brush-drawing in the remarkable face of Lo-han. In any case, "wild" and "unorthodox" do not imply any lack of capability. It was this style of free and independent character which Chinese painters took up again in the middle of the last century, above all Jen Po-nien who left a number of paintings full of humor. Like his predecessors of the seventeenth century, he too made use of blue and red, the colors of freedom, particularly in his album of portraits of poets. The portrait of T'ao Yuan-ming reproduced here (page 79) lacks the witty exaggeration of a painter like Chin Nung, though it does reveal a highly individualistic use of the brush.

Jen Po-nien's generation also included Wu Ch'ang-shih (1844–1927), the teacher of Ch'i Pai-shih (page 80). These men rediscovered, in a somewhat similar situation and with a similar spirit, the seventeenth-century Individualists. That the nineteenth and twentieth centuries produced no fewer great painters than the past is attested by the few examples given here of Jen Po-nien (page 79), Ch'i Pai-shih (page 80), Hsu Pei-hung (page 82), Chao Shao-ang (page 86), and Chang Ta-ch'ien (page 84), artists who are in every sense modern but who nevertheless belong to an ancient and still vital tradition.

The beginnings of Japanese art date from the same time as Japan's appearance in history, the sixth century of our era, when Chinese Buddhism made its way through Korea to gain influence in the island nation. The Regent Shotoku Taishi (552–621) adopted the new religion and gave his support to the Chinese missionaries. Although the early Buddhistic painting and sculpture of China have come down to us only in provincial examples of lesser quality, Japan has conscientiously preserved the art that China, its great master, rejected. To our great loss, the earliest paintings known, the seventh-century frescoes from the Kondo (Golden Hall) of the Horyuji in Nara, were burned after World War II through carelessness. Japan at the outset imitated fairly closely Chinese prototypes on all levels: public administration, city planning, temple architecture, sculpture, and painting. But with the passing of the T'ang Dynasty in China, such close relations declined and by the end of the ninth century contacts were limited to the formal exchange of ambassadors. In the centuries that followed, Japan, quite independently of China, developed its own more refined artistic conceptions.

The earliest Japanese painting reproduced here, which shows Buddha's entrance into Nirvana (page 87), was probably done after a Chinese prototype by Wu Tao-tzu whose depiction of this subject was famous in Eastern Asia. The Heian period (794–1185) was the most fruitful for Buddhist painting in Japan: esoteric Buddhism had become the dominant religion, and its artistic creations were still imbued with the force of conviction. The picture of Red Fudo (page 88) is one of the most significant works of that type.

With the close of the Heian period—also called the Fujiwara period (897–1185) after the most powerful family in the country— art acquired a courtly elegance in which subject matter became almost secondary to manner of treatment. The noble enthroned Buddha Shakyamuni (page 91), with his majestic bearing and elegant gold and red robe, is one of the most impressive works from that time. But then there arose the first completely original style of Japanese painting, the Yamato-e (the name devised to distinguish true Japanese painting from what preceded it). Buddhist texts from the Sutras, often with particularly beautiful title pictures, as well as nonreligious novels were illustrated on hand scrolls intended to be read from right to left in the same way as the script itself. China had known such hand scrolls, but they had never won the significance they enjoyed in Japan where they became the medium for the very finest narrative painting. The Genji-Monogatari scroll (page 95), which recounts the story of Prince Genji, numbers among the most beautiful works of this kind. The artist inserted the text of the novel in a fluent script between the individual illustrations, and these fragments of manuscript are the earliest texts known of the Tale of Genji. Not only do these pictures recount the story, but they also afford us a glimpse of the manners, costumes, and dwellings of the court 12 circles of the time. The painter removes, as it were, the roofs from houses to permit us to look in on the events taking place indoors, and this compositional device makes it possible to present several actions within a single picture. In similar scrolls of later periods, the illustrations became much more numerous and the text was separated from them. Such narratives in pictures were still being done in the Kamakura period (1185–1392) as is shown by the pictorial biography of the priest Ippen (page 102). But the figures were reduced in size and took second place to the landscape, and landscape itself became an independent subject, although it continued to have special significance. The *Nachi Waterfall* (page 104) is such a picture, at one and the same time a view of an actual place and a symbol of the divinity of nature.

The Kamakura period was marked by wars which began with Minamoto Yoritomo, who was named shogun or imperial field marshal, and who transferred the seat of government from Kyoto to Kamakura. During this time, relationships with China were resumed and Zen Buddhism was given an enthusiastic reception, by the military caste above all. Zen called for rigorous discipline and spiritual submission and taught, moreover, that enlightenment could be attained even in the daily round of practical living. Along with this Buddhist sect there came also from China a type of painting whose highest achievement was deemed to be tersely conceived pictures in India ink, either of landscapes or of themes drawn from the Zen teachings. Such an art corresponded to the spirit of the times in Japan and was taken up eagerly, even though it scorned all outward show. The greatest artist in this style of painting in ink, called by the Japanese Sumi-e, was beyond question Sesshu (1420–1506), who himself made several trips to China. The new style notwithstanding, it was the very realistically oriented Kamakura period which also produced the finest and most beautiful portraits. In China, ever since the Sung period, portrait painting was considered fit only for those who were merely painters by trade, and we know practically no examples of it. This is so much the more surprising in that, around 500, Hsieh Ho had laid down the classical formulation for Chinese aesthetics and art criticism, and it was equally applicable to portrait and figure painting. His theory was summed up in his famous Six Canons: (1) animation through spirit consonance, (2) structural method in the use of the brush, (3) fidelity to the object in portraying forms, (4) conformity to kind in applying colors, (5) proper planning in the placing of elements, (6) transmission of the experience of the past in making copies. Just as ancient Rome especially favored portraiture and achieved its highest perfection in that form, so too there are outstanding examples in Japan. The most significant is certainly that of 13

Yoritomo painted by a distinguished nobleman of the house of Fujiwara, then already in decline (page 98). With a realism carefully held in check, the painter produced a completely convincing portrait of the first imperial marshal in Japanese history. An earlier example, from the Heian period of the middle of the eleventh century, the portrait of the Chinese priest Jion Daishi (page 90), was painted after a Chinese prototype. Still in the courtly tradition of the Fujiwara is the portrait of Kobo Daishi sunk in profound meditation but nevertheless presented as a charming child (page 92). The idealized portrait of the poetess Ko-ogimi (page 99), attributed to a son of Fujiwara Takanobu, is one of the most enchanting of the series of portraits of the thirty-six poets most highly honored and often depicted in Japan. This portrait is quite rightly numbered among the finest of its kind, with the refined woman poet in a graceful pose, her garments decoratively displayed. The last of the outstanding portraits reproduced here is that of the poet Sogi (page 110): very close to the portrait of Yorimoto in its realistic conception, it is fully the equal of that masterwork in the subtlety of its means. The portrait did not die out in Japan but continued to be done right into the period of the great masters of the colored woodcut with their remarkable depictions of actors.

India-ink painting, which began in the Kamakura period, reached its perfect consummation in the Muromachi period (1392–1572), also known as the Ashikaga period. The shoguns of the house of Ashikaga returned the seat of government to Kyoto where they took up again the old traditions of court life. Two Ashikaga shoguns, Yoshimitsu (1358–1408) and his grandson Yoshimasa (1435–90), played a most important role in Oriental art through their passion for collecting. Both were lay priests of the Zen sect and sent monks and painters to China for the purpose of acquiring Zen ink paintings. To their particular affection for the art of the Southern Sung Academy we owe a number of outstanding Chinese pictures which the late Professor Speiser published in his *Meisterwerke chinesischer Malerei aus der Higashiyama Sammlung.* The Ashikagas' admiration for Chinese Zen painting was to have an enduring effect on Japanese art. Painters were urged and encouraged to try their hands at similar subjects. Sesshu is considered the most famous master of this style, and alongside him is ranked the somewhat younger Kei Shoki (c. 1478–1523; page 109) who did not himself visit China but, as director of the Geiami Gallery for Ashikaga Yoshimasa in 1478–80, had ample opportunity to study and copy the paintings there. Favorite subjects included not only landscapes but also the patriarchs of the sect, above all Daruma, its founder, whose powerful portrait by Soga Jasoku is reproduced here (page 108). Jasoku, a member of the warrior caste and a lay priest in the Zen sect, retired to a monastery in his old age, as did also the two Ashikaga shoguns.

Whereas the Ashikaga period was under the influence of China, the brief Momoyama period (1573–1615) led to a revival of purely Japanese art. Successors to the effete Ashikagas, the powerful generals Nobunaga and Hideyoshi ruled the country with iron fists. Nobunaga himself did not live to enjoy the power he fought for, but Hideyoshi survived to build for himself, in the vicinity of Kyoto, the Momoyama Palace from which this brief but brilliant period takes its name. To embellish this and other palaces Hideyoshi brought in the finest artists of his time, and they produced those impressive decorative paintings which have become world-famous. The Kano masters excelled in making gleaming blue and gold folding screens, especially Eitoku who had learned how to work with ease on large surfaces from his teacher Motonobu, the founder of the Kano school. Flowers, birds, figures, and landscapes were the themes which in constantly renewed variations were used to cover the walls, utilizing rich gold backgrounds not only for their impressive splendor but even more to cast a shimmering light over everything.

A high point of this kind of painting was reached in the work of Sotatsu whose talent for decorative conceptions was not confined to large-scale paintings. In contrast to the often somewhat stiff and cold effect of the pictures of the Kano school, he introduced a new style of soft but colorful surfaces. In collaboration with his friend Koetsu, today famed chiefly as a calligrapher, he created pictures of extraordinary charm, one of the finest of these being the scroll with deer in the Seattle Art Museum.

If Sotatsu, with his pictures which revived the tradition of Yamato-e (pages 120, 121), was the perfect expression of Kyoto, his pupil Korin was the ideal painter of Edo and is acclaimed by many as the greatest genius in Japanese art. Edo—the present-day Tokyo—was the capital of the shoguns of the house of Tokugawa, and the time of their reigns, 1603–1868, is known as the Edo or Tokugawa period. It was a dynasty which brought the country three hundred years of peace and prosperity but, at the same time, isolation from the outside world and nearly the most efficient police state known through the years since then. The middle classes of Edo became wealthy and, lacking the special convictions peculiar to the warrior caste and the intellectuals, they found their pleasure in the things of daily life. They commissioned and bought pictures which corresponded to their own interests: actors, beautiful women, theater, and historical pictures as simple as those in popular illustrated books. The 15 colored woodcut was introduced, and with it came painters who exploited the Ukiyo-e themes, subjects drawn from the transitory world of human life. The first painter to turn out pictures that also satisfied the popular taste in woodcuts was Hishikawa Moronobu (page 125), whose portraits of beautiful women were used as models by many other artists.

But once again a wave of Chinese influence had a decisive effect on Japanese painting. This came from two sources: painters who were seduced by European realism, and others who admired the works of Wen-jen-hua which exemplified the literary art of the late Ming and early Ch'ing periods. The realists made the acquaintance of European copperplate engravings through the Dutch settlement in Nagasaki. Their foremost exponent was Maruyama Okyo who found the way to harmonize fidelity to nature with purely decorative conceptions, although this is perhaps less obvious in the picture of wild geese over the sea (page 132) than in the large pair of portable screens with snow-covered pines in the Mitsui Collection, Tokyo. Rosetsu was the most noteworthy of his pupils and can almost be classed as a master of witty realism (page 133).

The Bunjingwa painters, on the other hand, were conservatives for whom the traditional literature and painting of China sufficed and who used that older style to liberate themselves from the stifling disciplines of the studios. They championed a highly individual way of painting which is perhaps most evident in the works of Gyokudo (page 136) and whose last great master in more recent times was Tomioka Tessai (page 147). Japan's "modern era" began with the Meiji reforms of 1868 when the confining barriers fell and the country was opened to the outside world. When that happened, there was a passionate eagerness to adopt everything new from the West, and many Japanese would have been ready to sell their centuries-old treasures of art. Happily, an American, Ernest Fenollosa, appeared on the scene and succeeded in convincing the authorities to take legal measures for the protection and preservation of the culture of the past. The first public art school was founded—the Academy in Tokyo —and it was there that tradition and modernism were reconciled. An outstanding product of the Academy was Yokoyama Taikwan (pages 144, 146). Because of his perpetuation and mastery of the classical Japanese brush techniques he has come to be ranked among the most highly esteemed of modern artists.

In summary, then, China and Japan used the same means: India ink, a paint similar to our tempera, silk, and paper. With these, they both created superb and at the same time very different works of art. The two cultures were most closely related in two specific types of art, early Buddhist painting and India-ink painting, but in spite of all the influences from China the Japanese decorative sense produced a thoroughly indigenous art which belongs unmistakably to Japan itself.

Connoisseurs and scholars may perhaps regret the absence from these pages of many outstanding works known to them, but in assembling these examples it was the aim of the late Professor Speiser to give special prominence to the role played by color in painting of the Far East. For that reason he was particularly concerned that the painting of modern and recent times should be represented here in order to counter the notion that no significant art was produced in the Orient after the seventeenth century. He deliberately chose his examples from among those less frequently reproduced, and this conscientious approach was characteristic of all his work.

Two Hunting Scenes on a Fragment of a Lute · China, 4th century
B.C. · Lacquer on wood · From an excavation in Hsin-yang,
South Hunan, China

The wood of the lute was first covered with a black lacquer
ground, then, on this fragment, painted in lacquer with a scene
of two hunters carrying their quarry suspended from a staff
slung across their shoulders. Above them are two dogs, to the
right an animal resembling a bear, with a dog squatting on its
back and the point of a spear pressing into the bear from the
front. The painter's means were limited to flat silhouette style
with only three colors—bluish violet, flesh red, and yellow.
Here and there he laid one color over the other and then rubbed
the top one away to make a subtle transition from red to yellow,
as in the bear's head. The taut curves and silhouette style have
much in common with objects of the time in jade or bronze.

Filial Piety · China, 1st century A.D. · Lacquer on wood · Length, $15\frac{3}{8}''$ · From an excavation in Lo-Lang, Korea · National Museum, Seoul

This small pannier with separate lid was made in a laquer manu-factory in Szechwan and probably served as a gift to a minor colonial official. Geometrical motifs in red on a black ground are painted on the borders, and some of the corners are decorated with figures. The lid is ornamented by a frieze of figures depicting a theme much favored in the Han period, that of filial piety. The figures, in their colorful patterned garments, are well individualized. They are no longer rendered merely in profile and silhouette, but face each other in a diversity of positions and express themselves in lively gestures. From this product of an artisan's workshop we can glean some notion of what figure painting of the time must have been like.

Carriages and Horsemen · China, 2nd century A.D. · Fresco (detail)
· Height, $42\frac{7}{8}''$ · From a tomb in Liao-yang, Manchuria, near
Port Arthur

Carriages with court dignitaries attended by outriders gallop
across a landscape. The dominant colors are red and black. To
give an impression of depth, of nearness and distance, the figures
are disposed one above the other. Although the carriages are
drawn in three-quarter profile, thus allowing us to see their
passengers, some of whom are likewise in three-quarter profile,
the horses are rendered in pure profile. This limitation, combined
with their sweeping contour lines, recalls the earlier silhouette
style. However, similar depictions of carriages and horsemen are
found on the molded tiles and relief plaques from tombs of the
20 same period, especially in northern China.

Hunting Scene · China, c. 400 · Detail of a fresco in the Tomb of the Dancers · T'ung-kou on the Yalu River

Until 427, the capital of the North Korean Kokuryo dynasty was located in T'ung-kou on the middle Yalu. In the environs were many splendidly painted tomb chambers whose contents were despoiled long ago. The frescoes remain, however, and show the things that delight men in death as in life. Here, for example, are hunters on horseback, aiming their bows both forward and backward at deer and beasts of prey. Their horses seem to fly as they gallop, and this peculiarity, along with the special technique of aiming the bow, suggests some connection with the Near East. New in Chinese painting was the depiction of landscape through semicircular flat mountain forms rising directly from the ground, like flat pieces of stage scenery. We can be quite certain that fresco painting in China at the same period must have been much like this.

21

The Good Deeds of Buddha · Northwest China, c. 450 · Detail of
a fresco in the Caves of the Thousand Buddhas, Tun-huang

In many frescoes of the Caves of the Thousand Buddhas near
Tun-huang we find depictions of the Jataka, the fables of the
good deeds accomplished by Buddha before his birth into our
world. Here, in the so-called Ruru-Jataka, he appears as a golden
gazelle rescuing a despairing man who had thrown himself into
the water. At the left we see the rescued man astride the gazelle;
at the right he kneels in gratitude before the fabulous creature.
The landscape is built out of a number of elements like stage
flats which, for all their unrealistic coloring, clearly represent
small stratified mountain peaks. This kind of symbolic representation of landscape belongs to an ancient Near Eastern tradition,
22 and is found in Sassanian silver work of a later period.

Buddha and the Wild Animals · Northwest China, early 6th century ·
Detail of a fresco in the Caves of the Thousand Buddhas, Tun-
huang.

The cave temples of Tun-huang lie on the overland route to
India used by the Chinese Buddhist pilgrims. Along with
innumerable Buddhist statues, they contain brightly colored
frescoes. The surfaces are divided into horizontal bands by means
of fantastically colored trees and stage-wing-like rocky peaks.
The pictures must be read from right to left, like the later hand
or transverse scrolls so familiar in Eastern Asiatic art. In this
detail, the middle band shows two episodes from the earlier
existence of Buddha: in the first scene, impelled by his deep
compassion for all creatures, he throws himself off a rock as food
for the hungry young of a tigress; in the second, the tigress creeps
up on the lifeless body. The rocks serve not only as a horizontal
division but also to create a certain feeling of space. 23

Jataka Scene · Japan, beginning of 7th century · Side of the
Tamamushi Shrine · Lacquer on wood · Height, 25⅝″ · Horyuji,
Nara

The episode from the earlier existence of Buddha depicted here is
the same as that in *Buddha and the Wild Animals* (page 23), but here
the sequence must be read from top to bottom: Buddha hangs his
garment on a tree, then plunges down, and is devoured in a
bamboo grove by the tigress and her young. The filigreed
fittings at the corners were originally underlaid with iridescent
wings of the Tamamushi beetle—which is how the shrine came
24 by its name.

Landscape · Japan, first half of 8th century · Box lid · Painted in gold and silver on persimmon wood · $7\frac{1}{8} \times 15\frac{1}{4}''$ · Shosoin, Nara

The upper surface was first colored with a dye from the sap of the sapan tree and then painted in gold and silver (the plain strip of the upper border is an addition). The decoration of the lid is designed to be viewed from all four sides, at each of which is a separate small composition, complete in itself, but combining to form a single large composition. At each of the four sides there are rocky peaks in the conventional stage-flat shapes, but well articulated. These are painted in gold, as are the trees, mostly pines, whose tips are touched with silver. The landscapes are enlivened by a diversity of birds and by ruffling clouds rising up between the peaks. The handling of the birds and clouds reveals a kind of playful pleasure in animated brush drawing of a mastery we have not met with before this. Such painting would scarcely have come into being without Chinese prototypes. Most probably the Japanese artists who did this kind of work were pupils of Chinese or Koreans, if the latter themselves did not execute it. 25

Music in the Mountains · Japan, 8th century (traditional dating)
Painting on leather · Maximum dimensions, $16 \times 6\frac{1}{2}''$ · Shosoin,
Nara

This painting comes from the central part of the soundboard of
a large four-stringed lute *(biwa)*. To protect the soundboard from
the blows of the heavy plectrum used to pluck the strings, a band
of leather was glued across it which, as here, was then decorated.
On the white ground *(gofun)* of the leather, we see in the foreground a white elephant ridden by a bearded man of Indo-
Iranian type who beats a drum while three children dance and
play flutes. Through a cleft in the steep crags, in the center background, runs a watercourse, and behind it we see the sun setting
over the high horizon. A flock of birds flies toward the setting
sun. Because the painting was covered with a coat of varnish to
protect it from the strokes of the plectrum, the more delicate
shades of green, yellow, and various reds can scarcely be made
out. The sensitively conceived landscape with its animated painting
gives us a foretaste of what the finest Chinese painting of the
T'ang period was to be, and it is highly likely that this work was
done by a Chinese master.   27

Woman under a Tree · Japan, middle of 8th century · Detail of a wall screen · India ink and pale color on paper · Length of the face, 4½″ · Shosoin, Nara

This proud beauty with her rouged lips and rosy cheeks has tiny green beauty spots strategically placed on her forehead and on either side of her mouth to enhance the colors and animation of the face. She exemplifies the aristocratic ideal of beauty of the T'ang period in China, as we know it from many tomb figures. Even if the artist was himself Japanese, he followed Chinese models so closely that we can almost speak of a copy, perhaps of one of the unfortunately badly damaged pictures found in the oasis of Turfan in Central Asia.

The Tejeprabha Buddha and the Genii of the Five Planets · China, dated 897 · India ink and color on silk · $27\frac{1}{8} \times 20\frac{1}{2}''$ · From the Caves of the Thousand Buddhas, Tun-huang · British Museum, London

The Tejeprabha Buddha sits on a high two-wheeled chariot drawn over the clouds by two white oxen. The figures around the chariot represent the planets: Mercury in the background, an ape perched on his crown, holds up a brush and a writing tablet; to his left is Jupiter with a white boar's head as his chief ornament; the bearded, dark-skinned oxherd is Saturn; Venus plays a lute and wears a cock on her head; to her right stands Mars, a four-armed warrior-demon with sword, spear, and bow in his hands.

Domestic Scene · China, dated 1099 · Detail of a wall plainting ·
Total dimensions, c. 50 × 40″ · Pai-sha, Honan Province, China

The tile-faced tombs in Pai-sha contain innumerable frescoes
whose scenes from daily life were intended to guarantee happiness
for the deceased in the other world. This detail comes from the
west wall of the first tomb, which was discovered and excavated
in 1951–52. A distinguished couple sit on high stools at a table.
Behind each is a portable screen with lacquered frame and gilded
angle braces. On the table are wine cups with high saucers and
a tankard with ribbed body, very narrow neck, and modeled lid.
Objects like these, and like the vessels held by the male and
female servants, can be found in numerous collections of Chinese
and Korean ceramics of that period. In the Sung period, lifelike
genre scenes with figures were a favorite subject of even the
famous painters, though we know few original works of the
30 time.

Autumn Landscape · Northern China, 1031 · Detail of a wall painting from the mausoleum of Emperor Sheng-tsung · Total dimensions, 142⅞ × 119¼″ · Ch'ing-ling (Balin), Mongolia

The Liao or Khitan people who founded an independent kingdom in northern China were horsemen and hunters. One of the favorite hunting regions of Emperor Sheng-tsung (d. 1022) was in the Ch'ing-ling Mountains, and his son and grandson built him there a subterranean mausoleum of tiles. In the foreground of this wall painting of an autumn landscape, there is a bellowing stag on a knoll, birds in flight, and red-leafed trees. The lively coloring in the fantastic cloudbank, the trees and animals outlined in firm though not very vigorous brush strokes, both reveal the hand of a well-schooled painter.

Attributed to EMPEROR HUI-TSUNG (1082–1135) *Quail and Narcissus* · China · Leaf of an album · India ink and color on paper · $10\frac{5}{8} \times 16\frac{1}{2}''$ · Collection Asano, Kanagawa, Japan

Emperor Hui-tsung of the Sung dynasty, who ascended the throne at nineteen and reigned from 1101 to 1127, is not only the most famous but also the most significant of China's emperor-painters. Moreover, he is the first of the Chinese artists whose names we know and whose paintings have survived, though many more works have been attributed to him than one can be sure are from his hand, among them this quail near a narcissus plant. There exist many anecdotes about what a scrupulous observer of nature Hui-tsung was, and about how his attentive eyes never missed any detail. Nevertheless, no one would be tempted to consider as merely a realistic study from nature this picture done in a classical style characterized by confining the principal subject to a single corner of the composition. With the subtlest of brush techniques the artist contrasts the strong colors of the quail with the gentle sway of the narcissus to create an indelible impression of springtime. Had he been as secure and skillful a sovereign as he was painter and patron of the arts, his country might well have been spared war and conquest.

32

Attributed to CHAO CH'ANG *Bamboo and Insects* (detail) · China, c. 1000 · Color on silk · Total dimensions, 39 × 8¾″ · Collection Asano, Kanagawa, Japan

Chao Ch'ang, whose exact dates are unknown, is among the most highly esteemed flower painters of China. He did not belong to the Sung Academy, though he could not entirely resist the appeal of the subject matter and style of those masters. It is said of him that he painted the souls and not merely the outward forms of plants. In the varicolored profusion of insects and plants of this picture, the richly nuanced color is linked with a delight in detail and with a sure feeling for the distribution of colors. The gleaming red of the flowers and the white of the butterflies are not just accents of color in and for themselves, but also confer on the various shades of green an extraordinary brilliance which has survived intact through the centuries.

33

Mandarin Ducks beneath Peach Blossoms · China, late 12th century ·
India ink and color on silk · $41\frac{1}{2} \times 19\frac{1}{4}''$ · Museum, Shanghai

From early times in China, mandarin ducks in pairs have been a
symbol of marital concord, and this has been a favorite motif in
the various arts and crafts. Here, with a scrupulous precision that
must certainly be the work of one of the best painters of the
Southern Sung Academy, the ducks are placed together with
peach blossoms to symbolize not only connubial bliss but also
34 springtime.

Attributed to LI AN-CHUNG (c. 1090–1160) *Quail* · China · Leaf of an album · Color on silk · $9\frac{1}{2} \times 10\frac{5}{8}''$ · Nezu Museum, Tokyo

Li An-chung is one of the artists rather neglected in China, but in Japan, since quite early times, he has been very highly regarded, especially as a painter of quails. Many paintings in Japanese collections are attributed to him, and the present one is certainly among the finest of its kind. Whether it is correctly attributed to Li An-chung remains an open question, but there is no doubt that it is a brilliant example of the painting of the Southern Sung Academy, and it was not out of place in the great Higashiyama Collection to which it once belonged. In the division of the picture surface, almost half is left free, but the center is more emphasized than in the painting on the subject by Hui-tsung (page 32). Secure mastery in brush technique is revealed in the veins of the leaves as much as in the ebb and flow of the lines of the wavy ground on which the bird stands. The red of the buds, introducing a note of animation into the picture, shows the artist's subtle feeling for color.

LI TI (1089–after 1174) *Herdsman Returning Home through the Snow with a Hare* · China · India ink and color on silk · $9\frac{3}{8} \times 9\frac{5}{8}''$ · Yamato Bunka-kan Museum, Osaka

Li Ti was among the painters who, together with Kao-tsung, the nephew of the unfortunate Emperor Hui-tsung, fled across the Yangtse to the south, where they carried on the work of their academy in the new residence city of Hangchow. Kao-tsung, himself a painter, encouraged the arts at least as much as his uncle. Of the innumerable works of the Southern Sung Academy, a few found their way into the Higashiyama Collection, among them two pictures by Li Ti. These latter were painted as a pair, though each is complete and artistically valid in itself, as the example given here, the left-hand panel, proves. The composition left open on one side as well as the displacement of the center of gravity to a corner are entirely typical of the feeling for style of the period. The gray-toned empty sweep of the sky filled by the white of the snow-laden branches admirably expresses the chill and hostile winter's day, as does the humble figure of the herdsman with his ox.

Winter Landscape · China, late 12th century · India ink and pale color on silk · 50 × 21½″ · Konchi-in, Kyoto

In the past, as today, Chinese landscape painters were particularly fond of the seasons as a subject, and especially the cycle of all four seasons. Thus there is an autumn landscape from the hand of the same master who did this winter scene. The wanderer, in dark cowl and carrying a staff, has stopped in his path for a last look at the waterfall plunging down from snow-covered rocks and to listen to the cry of the apes in the tree above the water. The figure serves to lead our eye on, but is also an inseparable part of the landscape, as much so as the rocks and water. This is so not only because it is viewed from the back but, even more, because of its tiny proportions in relation to the whole.

Attributed to Su Han-ch'en (c. 1119–63) *Children Playing* ·
China · India ink and color on silk · 53⅞ × 29¾″ · Formerly
Collection Kawasaki, Kobe

Su Han-ch'en was a famous member of the Academy in Kaifeng
at the time of Hui-tsung. He fled with the Emperor's nephew to
Hangchow where his presence is documented even after the
abdication of Kao-tsung in 1163. Hangchow's gardens were
famous; because of them it was called the Heavenly City. Something of this paradisical feeling carries over into the painting done
there. Such a garden is seen here, with its flowering trees, decorative rocks, and peonies. The artist was no less skillful in
depicting the children in their gay-colored, richly patterned
38 garments.

The Homecoming of Wen-chi · China, 12th century · Detail of a hand scroll · India ink and color on silk · Height, 9⅞″ · Museum of Fine Arts, Boston

This scroll showing four episodes from the life of Lady Ts'ai Wen-chi is among the finest of the four surviving scenes from daily life by the Sung Academy painters. During the invasion of the Huns in 195, Lady Wen-chi was taken prisoner and deported. In captivity she married a Hun prince and bore him two sons. After twelve years she was permitted to return home. There exists a cycle of eighteen poems, traditionally ascribed to the Lady herself, which describe her life in the other land, her sorrowful farewell to her children, and the return to the cultured environment of her homeland. The detail shown here, her arrival at her own home, affords a glimpse of the busy life of a street in China: at the right, the dwelling of Wen-chi, in front of which the people who came to greet her are gathered in excited conversation; her carriage is hauled by oxen, and street vendors offer food to the men of the Lady's escort. The artist shows great subtlety in his use of the black of India ink to accent and enliven the colors.

LIU SUNG-NIEN (c. 1174–1230) *Palace Ladies in a Garden* · China ·
Leaf of an album · India ink and color on silk · $10\frac{1}{8} \times 10\frac{5}{8}''$ ·
Formerly Collection Kuroda, Tokyo

Liu Sung-nien came from the south, from Hangchow, and was
first a pupil and later a high official of the Academy which
awarded him the high honor of the Golden Girdle. Along with
Ma Yuan and Hsia Kuei he is reckoned among the greatest
painters of the turn of the century and his fame was based
equally on his landscape and figure painting. This small page
from an album shows once again the popularity of scenes from
domestic life in China at that period. The very subtle painting of
the ladies in their delicately patterned gowns with flowing shawls
recalls an artist like Chou Wen-chu (c. 970), who treated the same
subjects, though scarcely any original works of his have come
down to us. The figures are outlined with such precise brushwork that it would not be difficult to cut them out with scissors.
This by itself suffices to prove the artist's control and mastery of
his medium, but it is matched by a beautifully balanced use of
40 color such as can be expected only from a very great artist.

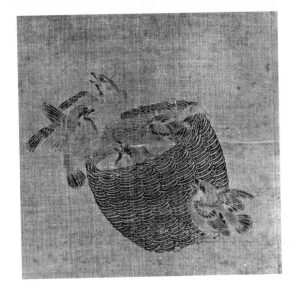

Attributed to SUNG JU-CHIH (c. 1260–80) *Sparrows in a Basket* ·
China · Leaf of an album · India ink and pale color on silk ·
$8\frac{5}{8} \times 8\frac{5}{8}''$ · Collection Asano, Kanagawa, Japan

Sung Ju-chih was another who came from Hangchow and was a
member of the Academy there. At the beginning of the Yuan
dynasty, in 1278, he entered a Taoist monastery. It is said that he
painted landscapes, figures, flowers and birds, but very few of
his works are known. This small page from an album, belonging
to an exquisite Japanese collection, may very well be ascribed to
him. In any case it is a precious example of the painting of the
late Southern Sung Academy done in the best academic style as
laid down by Hui-tsung. The finely balanced composition built
on a diagonal axis with its center of gravity almost in the middle
still leaves enough room on the tiny page to avoid any impression of crowding. The basket and birds are depicted in
animated fashion by strong, precise brush strokes, and the brown
of the sparrows' plumage is subordinated to the delicate shadings
of the black India ink.

Attributed to CH'IEN HSUAN (1235–c. 1302) *The Flute Player Huan Yeh-wang* · China · India ink and color on silk · 34 × 11¾″ · Formerly Collection Kawasaki, Kobe

Here we have one of the greatest of China's painters. It was said of Ch'ien Hsuan that he aspired to revive the art of the Northern Sung and T'ang periods, and among the paintings ascribed to him with some certainty, some at least are on subjects frequent under the T'ang dynasty. To what extent we have authentic works by Ch'ien Hsuan cannot as yet be proved. Certainly this portrait of Huan Yeh-wang corresponds to his period and style, and one need only observe the delicacy with which the loop of gauze on the hood is painted to know that it is a masterpiece.

Lu Chi (documented 1477–1505) *Winter* · China · India ink and color on silk · 69 × 39¾″ · National Museum, Tokyo

This winter scene belongs to a cycle of the Four Seasons with birds and flowers. A pair of pheasants is seen on the snow-covered bank of a stream, and there are plum trees in blossom with sparrows, bamboo plants, red camellias, and barberry shrubs. Energetically drawn, the stream winding through the mountains divides the composition asymmetrically. Lu Chi was one of the most famous artists of his time at the court of Peking, a highly skilled painter who came to exert great influence, especially on the eighteenth century.

44

FANG TS'UNG-I (documented 1338–77) *After the Rain* · China, dated 1349 · India ink and pale color on paper · 39 × 17″ · Collection King Kwei, Hongkong

Fang Ts'ung-i came from Kuei-ch'i in Kiangsi province. He was a Taoist and lived most of his life withdrawn from the world in the Shang-ch'ing temple on Lung-hu Mountain near his native town. At the upper left of the landscape is an inscription by the artist recounting that he painted this picture on the sixteenth day of the third month of spring in 1349. The longer inscription in two parts is a poem by the famous painter Wen Cheng-ming (1470–1559) written in 1535. The rain has stopped, but its haze lingers on above the river and twines like veils around the base of the mountain on the far bank. Despite its isolated prominence, the tiny figure in red on the shelf of rock in the foreground is there only as one more aspect of nature. The pagoda rising between trees on the left may belong to the Shang-ch'ing temple, and the view over the river may well be one familiar to Fang Ts'ung-i during his many years of seclusion; however, the artist's aim was to portray not any specific place but rather the essence of nature as revealed in the landscape. 45

SHEN CHOU (1427–1509) *The Mighty Mount Lu* · China, dated 1467 · India ink and pale color on paper · 76¼ × 38⅝″ · Palace Museum, Taichung, Taiwan (Formosa)

Shen Chou, one of those known as the Four Great Painters of the Ming period, belonged to a prominent family in Soochow. He passed the state examination, but disdained an official position, preferring instead to remain in Soochow and indulge his inclinations. He became famed as a calligrapher, painter, and poet, and was friendly with most of the scholars and artists of his time. This mountain landscape embodies a powerful compositional scheme which begins with the topmost peak and runs down in a bold S-curve to come to rest in the splendid clump of pines in the lower foreground. The energetic, transcendent spirit of a great painter is revealed in the brushwork of the extremely subtle calligraphic lines in the trees, the contours of the separate crags, and the waves of the stream. It appears also in the powerful accents of stippling such as that on the highest mountain peak (the latter a technique for which Shen Chou was especially famed). The tiny spots of color on the trees jutting out between the rocky crags are subordinate to the wide scale of tonal values of India ink which is the basic medium of the painting, because they intensify the suggestion of color inherent in that scale.   47

YAO SHOU (1423–95) *Red Plum Blossoms* · China · Hand scroll ·
India ink and color on paper · $15\frac{5}{8} \times 48''$ · Collection King
Kwei, Hongkong

The family of Yao Shou was of some importance in Chia-shan
in Chekiang province, and his father, Yao Fu, had a certain
reputation as a painter. Yao Shou passed the highest state
examinations and for a time, in his mid-sixties, had an official
position. But he left public service and returned to his native
place where he built a house whose name came to be identified
with his, so that he was called the Master of the Cinnabar Hill.
He belongs among the painters of the early Ming dynasty who
continued to work in the tradition of the Yuan period, and the
three great painters of that period, Wu Chen, Wang Meng, and
Chao Meng-fu, were the models he chose. Besides being a painter
he was also a poet and an excellent calligrapher. In China, plum
blossoms together with bamboos and pines constitute the "Three
Friends of the Cold Season," since their flowering begins when
snow is still on the ground. Even without an inscription, the
artist's skill as a calligrapher shows in every line of the energetically curving branch which, with the delicate rose of its
blossoms, is in contrast with the gnarled tree trunk the artist has
painted by overlaying areas of wet color.   49

CH'IU YING (c. 1500–1550) *Two Houseboats with Gentlemen and Ladies* · China · Leaf of an album · India ink and color on silk · $9\frac{1}{2} \times 9\frac{1}{2}''$ · Formerly Collection Kuroda, Tokyo

Of the "Four Great Painters of the Ming Period"—Shen Chou, T'ang Yin, Wen Cheng-ming, and Ch'iu Ying—the latter was the youngest. Unlike the other three, he did not come from landed gentry and earned his bread mostly as a lacquer painter and a copyist of T'ang and Sung pictures. He came from T'ai-ts'ang in the outer environs of Shanghai but, like his three associates, lived most of his life in Soochow. T'ang Yin's teacher, Ch'en, discovered the young man's talent and took him as a pupil, as did later T'ang Yin himself, with whom Ch'iu Ying enjoyed the deepest friendship. Ch'iu Ying's preference for scenes from everyday life may derive both from his teacher and from prototypes of the T'ang and Sung periods. The excellence of this small painting, which bears the artist's seal, explains why he is ranked alongside the famous figure painters Chou Wen-chu (c. 961–75) and Su Han-ch'en (page 38).

WEN CHENG-MING (1470–1559) *The Studio at Chen Shang* · China, dated 1549 · Detail of a hand scroll · India ink and pale color on paper · Total dimensions, $14\frac{1}{8} \times 42\frac{1}{2}''$ · Museum, Shanghai

Wen Cheng-ming (Wen Pi) belonged to a family of scholars and public officials in Soochow. He lived for a time in the capital, Peking, where, as an associate of the Han-lin Academy of Literature, he helped compile and edit the official history of the Yuan dynasty. Soon, however, he returned to his homeland to devote the rest of his long life to painting, poetry, and calligraphy. He had a large circle of students and friends, and his painting continued to be influential right up to the late sixteenth century. For his friend Lord Hua Hsia, a famous collector of the time, Wen Cheng-ming painted this scroll showing his own studio, a subject he took up again eight years later. This detail shows the house open on the garden, and in it two distinguished gentlemen looking at some writing while a boy serves them. The weirdly shaped garden rocks and the gnarled pine trees are a good indication of this artist's fine brushwork. The tiny red spot of a stool suffices to intensify the delicate blue of the rocks and mountains, the green of the pines, and the brown of the tree trunks. 51

善和坊裏李端端　信是孃行
白牡丹花一朵　楊州　金滿市佳人
價反屬實酸唐寅

T'ANG YIN (1470–1524) *Domestic Scene* · China · India ink and color on paper · 58¾ × 26″ · Palace Museum, Taichung, Taiwan (Formosa)

Like Wen Cheng-ming, T'ang Yin came from Soochow. His father was a modest tradesman, but the father of Wen Cheng-ming was willing to sponsor his son's gifted friend who had passed his examinations brilliantly but who, at the last moment, lost all chance of a position because of a scandal involving cheating. Disillusioned, the young man returned home and lived by painting. There he enjoyed the friendship of Shen Chou, Wen Cheng-ming, and Ch'iu Ying, and a life of wine and beautiful women—his reputation rests especially on his portrayals of the latter. The subject of this painting is a story of the T'ang period about the beautiful courtesan Li Tuan-tuan of Yangchow who attracted the attention of a poet and was praised by him in his poem "The White Peony Who Walks." Here she stands holding the white flower while the poet and her serving woman gaze at her. Two portable screens, set up to protect the beauty from the eyes of the curious and from the wind in the garden, reveal T'ang Yin's great talent as a landscape painter.

Tung Ch'i-ch'ang (1566–1636) *The Winding Valley* · China ·
Detail of a hand scroll · India ink and pale color on silk · 16 ×
267⅛″ · City Art Museum, Osaka

Tung Ch'i-ch'ang was a member of an eminent family of Hua-
t'ing who lived in Peking and on the Western Sea near Hangchow.
He was a minister, tutor to the crown prince, outstanding painter
and calligrapher, writer on art, collector, and connoisseur. The
influence of his powerful individuality can still be traced in the
following century. As a highly placed official he was often be-
seeched by friends for a picture—a practice quite common in
China. Naturally, he could not easily refuse these requests, which
is why not every work that bears his authentic signature is, in
fact, by his hand. Two of his pupils and friends, themselves
recognized painters, Chao Tso and Shen Shih-ch'ung, often
furnished him with a way out of such embarrassing situations.
This scroll, in linear style, is considered authentic and typifies
his classical insistence that each and every brush stroke be
complete and traceable from its beginning to its end. Such
completely linear drawing, especially that of the trees which
are only slightly emphasized by added color, reveals the hand
54 of a brilliant calligrapher.

Tung Ch'i-ch'ang *Hut beneath Crags* · China · Leaf of an album ·
India ink and pale color on silk · $10\frac{7}{8} \times 10\frac{3}{8}''$ · National Museum,
Tokyo

This landscape from an album containing six landscapes and ten
examples of calligraphy belongs, like the preceding scroll,
among the authentic works of this artist. When we examine these
two pictures, we can understand why Tung Ch'i-ch'ang's two
"ghost" painters had to divide their tasks into their separate
specialties: Chao Tso did the calligraphy, Shen Shih-ch'ung the
painting. Unlike the scroll in the previous plate, what dominates
in this landscape is less the linear than the formal element.
It has a freshness of conception often lacking in the drier
calligraphic approach. The foliage of the trees, delicately touched
with color, contrasts markedly with the broadly washed-in
mountains of the background. Yet, even at his most painterly,
Tung Ch'i-ch'ang never abandons his linear style, as shown by
the contrasts of the tree trunks and by the brush line which outlines the silhouette of the great mountain to the rear. 55

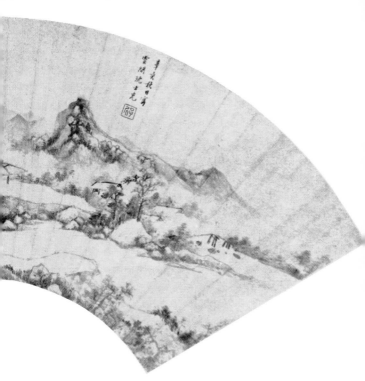

SHEN SHIH-CH'UNG (documented 1611–41) *Autumn Landscape* ·
China, dated 1611 · Leaf of a fan · India ink and pale color on
gold-speckled paper · $7\frac{7}{8} \times 22\frac{1}{2}''$ · Museum for Eastern Asiatic
Art, Cologne

Like the preceding artist, Shen Shih-ch'ung also came from
Hua-t'ing. His exact dates are not known, but he was a friend
and pupil of Chao Tso and of Tung Ch'i-ch'ang, for whom he
often painted pictures which the latter signed and gave as gifts.
Shen Shih-ch'ung ranks among the most charming artists of the
early seventeenth century, and in his calligraphically delicate and
yet strong linear drawing he shows himself a worthy pupil of his
master. In this clear autumn landscape, the open hut on the
foothill at the opposite side of the stream puts one in mind of the
great Yuan painter Ni Tsan (1301–74) whose unpeopled landscapes are characterized by such motifs. 57

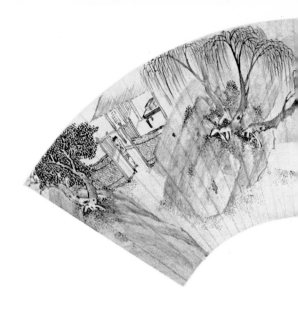

Li Shih-ta (documented 1574–1620) *Landscape with Figures*
China · Leaf of a fan · India ink and pale color on gold-speckled
paper · $7\frac{1}{8} \times 22''$ · Museum for Eastern Asiatic Art, Cologne

Li Shih-ta was a native of Soochow and passed the state examination, although it is not known if he ever held any official
position. Even in his lifetime he was famed as a figure and landscape painter. Narrative subjects like this were strictly taboo
for the classicists such as Tung Ch'i-ch'ang and his circle, but
had been familiar ever since the Sung period. Accompanied by
two servants carrying books, scrolls, and a parasol, the tall
gentleman rides toward his house where another servant waits for
him at the open door and where his books are already laid out
for him on the table. The landscape is impregnated with a feeling
of clarity and contemplativeness whose mood is well expressed
by the double line of writing at the edge of the fan: "In the
distance I see the weary-hanging willows of evening. In the house
I feel autumn enter in the midst of old mountains."

LAN YING (1585–c. 1664) *Autumn Landscape* · China, dated 1642 ·
Leaf of an album · India ink and color on gold-speckled paper ·
14⅛ × 13⅜″ · Collection Hoshijima

Another painter from a prominent family was Lan Ying of
Hangchow. He is considered the last follower of Tai Wen-chin
(c. 1430–50), who had revived the Sung style of painting and
founded the Chekiang school. He painted figures and landscapes,
flowers and birds, bamboos and rocks, often in the style of the
Southern Sung Academy though the great Yuan masters were
also his models. It is said of his pictures that the trees seem as if
the scurfy flesh of old witches had been pulled over them.
According to the inscription, the picture is meant to be in the
style of the Yuan painter Chao Meng-fu (1254–1322), but it has
about as much resemblance to its prototype as a statue by Rodin
has to one by Michelangelo. This picture impresses one by its
strong color. The malachite green of the patches of moss on the
stones combined with the gold of the heavily speckled paper
creates an immediate effect of brilliance such as was vigorously
60 banned by the classicistic circles of the period.

SHEN SHU-YU (documented 1667) *Winter Landscape* · China ·
Leaf of an album · India ink and pale color on paper · $10\frac{5}{8}$ ×
$12\frac{1}{8}''$ · Museum for Eastern Asiatic Art, Cologne

Shen Shu-yu lived in Hangchow, but practically nothing is
known of his life. What is more, scarcely enough works have
survived to make it possible to sum up his creative activity.
Nevertheless, we can recognize a painter of deep feeling in this
leaf from an album formerly containing eight landscapes, two of
which are now in Cologne. The verse inscription contains an
allusion to a poem about snow by Su Tung-p'o (1036–1101),
the most famous poet of the Sung dynasty and also a painter,
statesman, historian, and writer of high rank. But we have no
need of the poem to explain this winter landscape. The gray sky
heavy with snow fills the entire surface so that we cannot tell
where the sky leaves off and the sea begins. A man sits in the
pavilion enjoying his solitude and the view of the Western Sea
which is among Hangchow's many beauties. The green of the
pines makes one feel, by contrast, the cold of the snow whose
whiteness is further emphasized by the black patches against the
ice in the foreground.

TAO CHI (SHIH-T'AO) (1630–c. 1707) *Landscape* · China · Leaf of an album · India ink and pale color on paper · 10⅝ × 15¼″ · City Art Museum, Osaka

Tao Chi came from a side branch of the Ming Imperial House (family name, Chu), and is best known under the name he used as an artist, Shih-t'ao. Born in Chuan-chow in Kwangsi province, he became a monk in 1644 after the overthrow of the dynasty and undertook many voyages which led him into far-flung regions of China. In 1697, toward the end of his life, he settled in Yang-chow where he died around 1707. Along with Shih-ch'i, Pa-ta Shan-jen, and Hung-jen, he is reckoned among the "Individualists" of the seventeenth century, who refused to serve the new rulers and to wear, as a sign of subjection, the pigtail, and so had their heads shaved and became Buddhist monks. This painting from an album with twelve pictures reduces the landscape to its essential components. It must be a late work, painted with very powerful, even hard, but highly economical brush strokes. The predominant reds and blues—the colors of the free spirit—are contrasted with the strong accents of black in the trees on the right and in the cliffs.

TAO CHI (SHIH-T'AO) *The Glimmering Peak* · China · Leaf of an album · India ink and pale color on paper · $9\frac{5}{8} \times 6\frac{7}{8}''$ · Museum for Eastern Asiatic Art, Cologne

This picture belongs to an album with twelve views of Mount Lo-fou in southern China, each of which is accompanied by a written description on the facing page. The album was probably painted by Shih-t'ao on one of his voyages between 1660 and 1670. The very loose brushwork and the light coloring give no more than a hint of the powerful accentuation of his later work and suggest a relatively early date for the album. Three travelers melt into the landscape and become so much a part of the whole that at first one hardly notices them.

深山花滿兩
古寺暗紅泉
正紡此圖適當北刹深矣
四石當有临之敢佳也余因
因臨之
甲申三月朔 海寬黃□□

64

WANG HUI (1632–1717) *Deep in the Mountains* · 1692 · India ink and pale color on paper · 43¾ × 19⅛″ · Museum for Eastern Asiatic Art, Cologne

Wang Hui was a native of Ch'ang-su in Kiangsi province. His father was an art dealer, and so the young man had ample opportunity to see and copy paintings of the old masters. His teachers were Wang Shih-min (1592–1680) and Wang Chien (1598–1677), friends of Tung Ch'i-ch'ang whose classicistic conception they perpetuated. To this circle belonged also Wang Yuan-ch'i (1642–1715)—the youngest of the "Four Wangs" and grandson of Wang Chien—as well as Yun Shou-p'ing and Wu Li (1632–1718), the first educated Chinese to become a Catholic priest. The group came to be known later as the "Six Famous Painters of the Ch'ing Period," that is, of the seventeenth century. Wang Hui was the most prolific among them, and a great many of his pictures have come down to us. In his youth he was obliged to earn his living by painting, and that meant mostly copying, which probably explains how he came by the skill of imitating old masters so perfectly. The present picture, done in his old age, nevertheless betrays no hint of the facile routine of which he is often accused. The wry informative inscription reads: "Deep in the mountains fleet water falls; two old temples and hidden red wells. I saw such a picture by Chu-jan [c. 970] in the house of the Wu family in Ch'ing-hsi. The old Po-shih [Shen Chou] imitated the original perfectly. So I did likewise." This is a landscape to wander about in and to live in, as Kuo Hsi once expressed it. The figures, seen from the rear, with their soft red color which creates a bright point of contrast, not only invite us to observe the waterfall but also lead the eye along the path through the ravine up to the temple.

名谷此曾貌雁山積石而用牛指
思令此石恭宏致成骨高奇逾
出山雄氣槐格之外唐人逆秦倪以
見脉今初歓笛立其苞茲題日宋
惡遂塞亭為樣跋絵今傅於苫横
隆此説起日僅似與高所花绍
如甘人皸愈題歐良夷不鹿巳
庚八銭松世正五嶄旲人玉博此題

66

This great landscape is identified as a work by Wang Hui in a
long complimentary inscription by Wang Shih-min. Of Wang
Hui himself no signature or seal has come down to us. The
inscription is dated 1670, which can be taken as the date of the
picture. Up to the middle ground, the landscape is densely
filled with red-leaved autumn trees, between which there opens
at the left a steep path leading up to a mountain village with
straw-roofed houses. On the right the landscape becomes
more precipitous, and above the trees rises a temple enclosure with
fish-tail roofs and a pagoda. The picture is dominated by the
extraordinary mushroom-shaped mountain on the left which
towers above the valley and foothills. Its completely formed
shape, accented by the sparse vegetation, is the salient element of
the landscape and draws the eye up to it, while the counter-
movement of the red-leaved trees below leads toward the temple
at the middle right.

KAO YANG (documented 1623–36) *Spring Landscape* · Dated 1623 ·
Leaf of a fan · India ink and pale color on gold-speckled paper ·
$6\frac{1}{4} \times 19\frac{1}{8}''$ · Museum for Eastern Asiatic Art, Cologne

Kao Yang came from Ning-po, the harbor city on Hangchow
Bay in the province of Chekiang. He is known as a painter of
landscapes, birds, and flowers, but is especially famed for his
garden rocks. He collaborated on the "Collection of Calligraphies
and Paintings of the Ten-Bamboo Hall" ("Shih-chu-chai shu-hua
p'u"), a compendium of woodcuts for the student of painting,
and many of the examples for copying in it are by him. Late in life
he moved to Nanking where he specialized in landscapes. His
exact dates are not known, though he was probably still alive at
the beginning of the Ch'ing period in 1644. It can be presumed
that this fan comes from his years in Nanking. The tall gentleman
on the left, crossing a bridge which leads to a temple, is a common
motif in Chinese landscape painting. But this figure does not
invite us to join him in contemplating nature's beauties, but instead
to follow his wanderings, though the path he must take soon
disappears behind the cliffs. Indeed, the wanderer taking his
first step across the bridge is so peripheral to the broad landscape
that one scarcely notices him as one's eye travels over the mountain spurs to the gleaming pale blue distance.

YANG CHIN (1644–1728) *Landscape* · Dated 1674 · Leaf of an album · Gold on blue paper · $8\frac{5}{8} \times 6''$ · Museum for Eastern Asiatic Art, Cologne

Yang Chin was from Ch'ang-shu in Kiangsi province like Wang Hui, with whom and for whom he worked. His subjects were landscapes, birds and flowers, figures and portraits. This picture is from an album with five landscapes and calligraphies done in gold on a gleaming cobalt-blue background. Two islets of reed and a boat headed toward land soften the effect of emptiness of the broad surface of water. Even more than the figure in the boat, the house half-hidden by the trees in the foreground shows that the homecomer is no simple fisherman but a great gentleman.

YUN SHOU-P'ING (1633–90) *Flowering Branch* · Leaf of an album ·
India ink and color on paper

Yun Shou-p'ing was a native of Wu-chin in Kiangsi province.
His uncle Yun Hsiang (1586–1655) was a recognized landscape
painter, and his teacher Wang Shih-min also taught Wang-hui,
Yun Shou-p'ing's lifelong friend. Yun Shou-p'ing is the most
sensitive in feeling of the "Six Famous Painters of the Seventeenth Century." Landscapes are rare among his production, and
his fame rests on the special style of his flower pictures which,
even in his lifetime, were counterfeited. For the most part he
painted only in pale colors without the "bony framework" of
outlines in India ink; this technique was known in China as far
back as the sixth century although no early examples have survived. The flowering branch seen here is done in the "boneless"
style, which explains the almost fragrant delicacy of the blossoms. The leaves are painted with such control and subtle rhythm
as to make us not even miss the usual "skeleton" of ink, and their
green and orange coloring makes a delightful contrast to the
rose and gray of the flowers such as only a great painter can
achieve.   71

LANG SHIH-NING (1688–1768) and T'ANG TAI (1673–1752)
Emperor Ch'ien-lung on Horseback · Dated 1744 · Detail of a hand
scroll · India ink and color on silk · Total dimensions, $18\frac{1}{8}$ ×
$96\frac{5}{8}''$ · Fujii Yurin-kan Museum, Kyoto

Lang Shih-ning, whose real name was Giuseppe Castiglione,
was an Italian Jesuit missionary who came to China in 1719. His
talents in painting won him the respect of Emperor Ch'ien-lung
who named him court painter, especially for portraits. Lang's
collaborator T'ang Tai was, like him, a foreigner, a high Manchu
dignitary. T'ang learned his art with some success from Wang
Yuan-ch'i and himself wrote a treatise, "A Demonstration of
Fine Subtleties in Painting." To this scroll, done together with
Castiglione, whose full title is "The Emperor's Inspection of His
Horses on a Meadow in Spring," T'ang Tai contributed his
specialty, the landscape, while the Italian painted the dignified
portraits of the Emperor on horseback and his attendant. Lang's
figures, painted directly without any ink drawing, appear against
T'ang's colorful background in shades of green and both delicate
72 and strong rose.

TSOU I-KUEI (1686–1772) *Cranes and Peonies* · India ink and color on paper

The family of Tsou I-kuei were officials and scholars in Wu-hsi in Kwangsi province. After passing the examinations with highest honors, he became not only court painter but also the Emperor's adviser on questions of taste. As inspiration for his landscapes he chose the Yuan painters Ni Tsan and Huang Kung-wang, but his flower paintings—the chief source of his fame—are said to be in the style of Yun Shou-p'ing (page 71). But, at the wish of the Emperor, he also studied European painting with the Jesuits, and as a result he rendered flowers with virtually scientific accuracy.

TUNG PANG-TA (1699–1769) *Landscape* · Fan · India ink and pale color on silver paper · $9\frac{1}{2} \times 26\frac{3}{4}''$ · Museum for Eastern Asiatic Art, Cologne

Tung Pang-ta belonged to the Fu-yang circle in Chekiang, took the state examinations, and became court painter under Emperor Ch'ien-lung (1736–96). He was also curator of the imperial collection of paintings and bronzes and one of the compilers of its catalogue. His pictures are often in the style of the great artists of the tenth century: this fan, with its dense profusion of mountains and trees leaving almost no free space, recalls the work of Tung Yuan. However, his models were taken just as much from the Yuan painters, in accordance with the express wish of his imperial employer. Thus, in only a few pictures did he reveal that his talents extended beyond this sort of imitation of the past.

Wang Ch'eng-p'ei (c. 1725–1805) *Two Birds on a Plum Tree with Bamboo* · Color on blue-painted paper · $22\frac{1}{4} \times 6\frac{7}{8}$" · Museum for Eastern Asiatic Art, Cologne

Wang Ch'eng-p'ei was a member of a family of officials and scholars in Hsiu-ning, Anhwei province, and his father was a well-known painter and poet. He himself passed two examinations and, like Tung Pang-ta, was called to the court as a painter. There he did figures, landscapes, flowers and birds, and followed his father also as poet and writer. Only a few of his pictures are known. Just as Emperor Ch'ien-lung desired Castiglione to learn the Chinese way of painting, so also did he require his own Chinese court painters to acquaint themselves with European techniques. The product of this double training was painting such as this, in which Wang Ch'eng-p'ei tried to reconcile the two worlds of art. Despite its evident European traits, this plum branch recalls the compositions of the Sung school: almost two-thirds of the background is left blank, though the white of the birds seems to raise the center of gravity above the lower left corner.

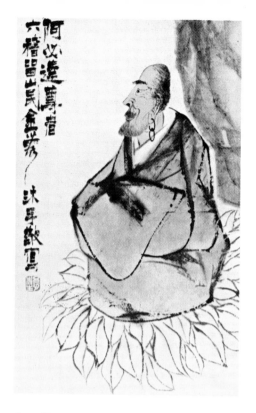

CHIN NUNG (1687–1764) *Lo-han* (detail) · India ink and pale color on paper · Total dimensions of scroll, $37\frac{1}{4} \times 10\frac{3}{4}''$

Although he lived in Yangchow, Chin Nung came from Hangchow. He was a poet and writer, but at fifty he began to paint. With coarse, bold brush strokes Chin Nung has outlined this figure of Lo-han, a disciple of Buddha, seated on a throne of leaves before a wall of rock. The rock is thinly washed in, its form implied but not set down in detail. Colors which are soft but clear contrast with the heavily accentuated black of the contour drawing and the inscription, while the leaves, though stylized and disciplined, are painted with an almost delicate verve. All the subtlety of drawing is concentrated on the face to reveal its extraordinary, grotesque but spiritual humorousness.

JEN PO-NIEN (1840–95) *The Poet T'ao Yuan-ming* · Dated 1887 ·
Leaf of an album · India ink and pale color on paper · $10\frac{1}{8}$ ×
$13\frac{3}{8}''$ · Museum for Eastern Asiatic Art, Cologne

Jen I, better known under his name as an artist, Jen Po-nien,
came from Shao-hsing in Chekiang province but lived mostly in
Shanghai. He was among those who rediscovered the "Individualists" of the seventeenth century and is acclaimed as a pioneer
of modern art in China—his grandson and pupil is Ch'i Pai-shih.
This picture belongs to an album which formerly had eight
paintings, six of which are now in the Cologne museum, all of
them portraits of China's famous poets. Here we see the poet
T'ao Yuan-ming (365–427) returning home in a boat with
chrysanthemums. The figure of the poet is outlined in somewhat
nervous brush strokes, whereas the boy behind the gnarled tree
trunk seems to be painted with dabs of ink. Blue and red in both
delicate and strong tones lend animation to the figures set against
the broad empty expanse of water in the middle ground.   79

CH'I PAI-SHIH (1863–1957) *Lemons* and *Persimmons* · Both 1926 · India ink and color on paper · Each 52 × 13″ · Museum for Eastern Asiatic Art, Cologne

Ch'i Huang, who as an artist used the name Ch'i Pai-shih, came from the small town of Hsing-tse-wu in Hunan province. Of poor family, he worked as a carpenter. But already in his early years he painted for his own pleasure, though he did not learn to write until later—an unusual sequence in China—when the scholar Wang Hsiang-chi taught him his letters and the painter Wu Ch'ang-shih his art. Ch'i Pai-shih learned more, in fact, from nature than from the classical models. In early manhood he was able to give up his carpenter's trade and support his family by selling his pictures. Fame reached him, however, only after showing in the Berlin Sezession exhibition of 1930, when word of his European triumph filtered back to China. His unusual personal background and unconventional way of painting have made him a model for the recent and present generations of painters in China. These two pictures, now in Cologne, were acquired directly from the artist by Professor Otto Fischer in 1926 in Peking where Ch'i Pai-shih lived from 1920 until his death. Their fascination lies in their gleaming colors, a quality for which this artist has always been acclaimed. In contrast to the graduated tones of ink used for the leaves, the fruit is painted in the "boneless" manner as bright and undetailed globes of yellow and red.

82

HSU PEI-HUNG (JU PÉON) (1894–1953) *Horse under Willows* ·
Dated 1936 · India ink and pale color on paper · $41\frac{3}{4} \times 14''$ ·
Collection Mrs. Renate Berk, Neuhemmerich bei Köln (Cologne)

Hsu Pei-hung was born in I-hsing in Kiangsi province, an
ancient center of ceramic-making, and studied in Shanghai and
Japan. After World War I, he attended the École des Beaux-Arts
in Paris between 1919 and 1923, and until 1927 traveled much
in Europe, spending considerable time in Berlin and Vienna.
In 1932 he again traveled about Europe, presenting exhibitions
under his French name Ju Péon, and in 1937–38 he visited
southern and southeastern Asia. He became a professor in
Nanking, and from 1947 to his premature death he was presi-
dent of the Academy in Peking. He harmonized European
modes of seeing with Chinese technique to make a highly
personal style which, nevertheless, is not false to the classical
traditions in which he was trained. His pictures of horses have
become known throughout the world as examples of modern
Chinese painting. In this picture of a young horse, which is
dedicated to the elder brother of the painter Chang Ta-ch'ien,
the mastery of brushwork as seen in the bare branches and boughs
of the willow tree reveals the hand of a great painter. By gradu-
ating the ink from pale gray to deep black, the horse is made to
stand out strikingly against the colored ground at its feet.   83

CHANG TA-CH'IEN (1899–   ) *Landscape* · Dated 1945 · India ink and pale color on paper · $31\frac{7}{8} \times 15\frac{3}{8}''$ · Museum for Eastern Asiatic Art, Cologne

A native of Neikiang in Szechwan province, Chang Ta-ch'ien now makes his home in South America after having traveled extensively in China, Japan, Europe, and America and gained international fame. He owes most to the seventeenth-century "Individualists" but has not ignored the lessons of the Sung and T'ang masters—he has copied the frescoes in Tun-huang with such skill that his copies almost surpass the originals in general favor. He is also a collector of pictures of every style and period, though there have been rumors that some of them were painted by the master himself. His is a completely cosmopolitan spirit, and there is a vast diversity of expression in his pictures. Even when he seems to be painting in the style of Shih-t'ao, he gives his own creative character to the spirit and brushwork of that master. Among his friends are many outstanding painters, including Picasso with whom he exchanges pictures and ideas. This picture combines the delicacy of a Yuan landscape with the artist's own feeling for color as expressed in the pale blue-green mountains and trees and the brown of the sand bar. The tiny figures of the wanderer and his servant under the trees in the foreground are seen from the rear and blend with the vegetation to such an extent that they give no pause to the eye as it travels to the distant hill.

CHAO SHAO-ANG (1904–   ) *Kingfisher on a Flowering Branch* ·
Dated 1934 · Leaf of an album · India ink and paint on paper ·
$11\frac{1}{2} \times 14\frac{5}{8}''$ · Collection Mrs. Renate Berk, Neuhemmerich bei
Köln (Cologne)

Chao Shao-ang comes from the cosmopolitan city of Canton and
studied under the painter and writer Kao Chien-fu. In his
paintings, as in those of his teacher, French Impressionism is
blended with the ancient traditions of China. Here, on a gnarled
tree, a kingfisher perches and from the right projects a branch
of blossoms. Chao's picture is notable for the way paint and ink
are used, with shadings which give form to the tree, flowers, and
leaves and which make the kingfisher stand out brightly and
prominently. The delicacy of the buds and flowers is balanced by
the strong accents of the tiny spots of black ink on the trunk and
leaves. The tension of the small bird is conveyed by its eye and
beak which are outlined by forceful brush strokes. There is
nothing accidental, nothing unnecessary in the composition;
86 everything is executed with a sure and masterful hand.

Death of Buddha · Dated 1086 · India ink, color, and gold on silk ·
105⅜ × 106¾″ · Kongobu-ji, Koyasan

This composition of the death of Buddha, or his entry into
Nirvana, is the most ancient surviving painting on this moving
theme in Japan. Buddha lies in the center beneath blossoming
Sala trees; at his head kneel Bodhisattvas; the entourage of
Devas (watchmen and demigods) surrounds him, with figures
from the human world nearby and, in the foreground, a lion as
symbol of the animal kingdom. Above the trees appears Maya,
mother of Buddha Shakyamuni, who has been resting in the
abode of the gods since her death. There is a contrast between the
restrained mourning of the Bodhisattvas and the vivid grief of
the other figures.

Fudo Myoo (Red Fudo) · 10th–12th century · India ink, color, and gold on silk · 65 × 36⅞″ · Myoo-in, Koyasan

Of the five tutelary Buddhist gods Fudo is the most important. He is regarded in Japan as the manifestation of the principal Buddha of the mystic sects, the Dainichi Buddha. As a champion against Evil, he counteracts it by assuming an even more frightening appearance. As the "Indestructible One" he is seated on crags from where he binds and slays Evil with his dragon-encompassed sword and rope; his halo is a blaze of flames. Mystical Buddhist religious paintings are subject to the strictest iconographic rules which were nonetheless infringed by the artists. This representation of Fudo is among the most vigorous paintings of the Heian period.

Nagarjuna at the Iron Stupa · First half of 12th century · Color and gold on silk · 70 × 55⅝″ : Fujita Museum, Osaka

Nagarjuna is one of the patriarchs of mystical Buddhism (Shingon), to whom, according to the legend of the Iron Stupa in South India, the esoteric doctrine of Vajrasattva was revealed. The painting refers to the legend: the Stupa is set in an unreal landscape such as we know from the Chinese T'ang paintings. Layer-like mountain formations shift from shades of green to pale blue and the delicate flowering plants and trees suggest spring. The effect of the landscape is produced above all by its stratified forms which seem to be achieved almost without brush strokes, while the artist reveals an extremely fine use of line in the details, in the blossoms and leaves of the plants, in the superstructure of the Stupa, and in the sensitive delineation of the figures and the folds of their costumes.

Portrait of Jion Daishi · Middle of 11th century · Color and India ink on silk · $63\frac{3}{8} \times 50\frac{3}{8}''$ · Yakushi-ji, Nara

Jion Daishi was a famous Chinese priest of the T'ang dynasty, who was especially honored by the Japanese Hosso sects. On the anniversary of the death of the patriarch the temple of Yakushi-ji, a center of this Buddhist cult, organized ceremonies at which special prayers were recited before the present picture. We can assume a Chinese model for this portrait, a fact that is demonstrated by such details as the small table on the right with the writing implements and, on the left, the water jug, which give us an insight into the life of a Chinese monk of the T'ang dynasty. Despite such influences, this painting impresses us as an entirely individual work of art; crowning the starkly contrasting colors of the robe, we see the powerfully modeled face of a dominating personality, with eyes which lend vitality to the whole figure.

Buddha Shakyamuni · c. 1000 · Paint, India ink, and gold on silk · $62\frac{3}{4} \times 33\frac{5}{8}''$ · Jingo-ji, Kyoto

The exalted Buddha on his lofty lotus throne, with the red robes which give the picture its alternative title *Aka Shaka (Red Shaka)*, is a noble representation which, though perhaps lacking in forcefulness, prevails all the same by virtue of its gentle beauty. The soft red of the robes is overlaid by a delicate pattern in incised gold leaf *(kirikane)*, which is given a particular luminosity by the vivid green border. Rays from the head of the Buddha break through the halo of painted golden flowers encircling his face, which expresses graceful serenity.

Kobo Daishi as a Boy (detail) · Late 13th century · Paint, silver, and India ink on silk · Total dimensions, $30\frac{3}{8} \times 16\frac{3}{4}''$ · Collection Maruyama, Mikage

According to a legend, Kobo Daishi, when a boy, dreamed that he was sitting on an eight-leafed lotus throne in discussion with various deities about the principal features of Buddhism. Characteristic of the courtly style, the legend inspired paintings such as this showing one of the most important priests of his time, the founder of the Shingon sect, as a child (Chigo Daishi). Here we see him as a delightful, bright-faced boy sharply delineated and with a vitality which is emphasized by the severe frame of dark hair. Black trousers and a white robe, the silver flower pattern of which has oxidized to gray, accentuate the elegant figure.

Title picture of Yakuso-Yubon Scroll · Completed 1141 · India
ink, color, and gold on paper · 10 × 8⅜″ · Collection Muto, Kobe

As well as Buddhist religious paintings, the late Heian period also
gave us the E-Makimono (hand scrolls with narrative content),
which were commissioned or even created by lords and ladies of
the court. The Yakuso-Yubon scroll belongs to the Hokkekyo
Sutra series, which was donated in 1141 by nobles and ladies of
the court of the Emperor Toba to the no longer preserved
Kunoji temple in Suruga. The title picture represents the realm
of Buddha compared with that of man. With his rain, Buddha
gives new life to the parched earth and the plants. In the foreground a gentleman sits under his umbrella enjoying the rain. 93

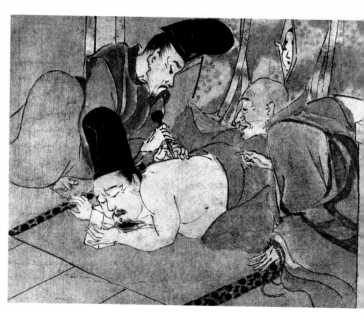

The Scroll of the Sicknesses (Yamai-no-soshi) · Late 12th century
· India ink and color on paper · $5\frac{1}{2} \times 7''$ · Yamato Bunka-kan
Museum, Nara

In addition to the representation of the refined world of the
court, there also exists among the Yamato-e scrolls a number of
paintings which deal with the perils and needs of human existence. Among these are the Sickness Scrolls where the people
represented are generally of humble station. This small fragment
shows acupuncture being applied to a corpulent man whose pain
can be read in his face. The "doctor" wields his instrument with
an aloof expression, refusing to be influenced by the priest holding
the prayer beads or the woman in the background. Compared
with the other existing Yamai-no-soshi Scrolls, the figures are
too large in relation to the height of the paper, though the original
measurements of the fragment cannot be reconstructed. There is
no doubt that this painting is not the work of the artist who did
the other scrolls, even if in liveliness of expression it does not
94 fall short of the other representations of this theme.

Genji Scroll, chapter 39: Yugiri (detail) · First half of 12th century · India ink and color on paper · Dimensions of detail, $8\frac{5}{8} \times 11\frac{5}{8}''$ · Collection Masuda, Tokyo

The Genji-Monogatari, or the Tale of Prince Genji, was written around 1000 by the lady-in-waiting Murasaki Shikibu. Of the scrolls illustrating the novel (the Genji-Monogatari-Emaki) four are in existence today, and they rank among the finest of the Yamato-e. Here we see Yugiri, the son of Prince Genji, who has fallen in love with the widow of his friend. The latter's mother writes to him that she wishes to give her daughter to him. But his wife, Kumoi-no-kari, has begun to have suspicions and surprises him as he reads the letter. From the black writing case open in front of him one can suppose that he intended to reply to the letter at once. The artist lets us see into the house from above; he has, as it were, removed the roof, with the result that we can also look into the adjoining room. The contours in India ink display, in the figures especially, a delicate play of line, but this is subordinated to the careful balance between gray and red.

Nezame Scroll (detail) · Late 12th century · India ink, color, gold, and silver on paper · Total dimensions of scroll, $10\frac{1}{8} \times 200''$ · Yamato Bunka-kan Museum, Nara

The Genji Scrolls and the Nezame-Monogatari-Emaki number among the finest achievements of the Yamato-e style (the "Japanese" style). The Nezame Scroll, with its clear coloring and rich use of patches of gold and silver—in part made from cut-out foil *(kirikane)*—tends perhaps more toward decorative effect. The figures are smaller than in preceding scrolls, and take second place to the landscape. For this reason it is certain that the painting was done later than the Genji Scroll. This title picture for the first scene gives us a glimpse of a Japanese landscaped garden of the time. Blossoming cherry trees and meadows are decoratively but naturalistically presented, while the blue and brown costumes of the lady playing the flute and her attendant form a lively 96 contrast to the enchanting garden.

Kitano Tenjin Engi (detail) · First half of 13th century · India ink and color on paper · Total dimensions of scroll, $20\frac{1}{2} \times 372\frac{1}{8}''$ · Kitano Temman-gu, Kyoto

In this scroll, the life of the loyal statesman Sugawara no Michizane (845–903) is portrayed. He was deified as Temman Tenjin and the Kitano Temman-gu was consecrated to him. This detail is from the first of eight scrolls and shows a discussion between the young Michizane and his father Sugawara Koreyoshi. We look down on the carefully laid-out garden surrounded by buildings. In the background, on the outer porch, the boy sits facing the Prince who is in an open room. The unknown artist meticulously depicted the garden with a dark blue stream running zigzag through it. Stepping stones and rocks overgrown with moss make bridges and rock crannies, while tiny low chains of hillocks form the boundary in the foreground. Trees in blossom tell us that it is spring, while a few dark pines, such as are invariably included in Japanese paintings, make a lively point of emphasis in the background.

FUJIWARA TAKANOBU (1142–1205) *Portrait of Minamoto Yoritomo* ·
India ink and color on silk · 55½ × 44¼″ · Jingo-ji, Kyoto

Fujiwara Takanobu was not only a prominent nobleman in
Kyoto, but also a brilliant portrait painter. This portrait is one of
a series which originally included four—all of friends of Emperor
Goshirakawa—commissioned for the palace erected in 1188 for
the abdicated ruler. The portrait of Minamoto Yoritomo is one
of the most famous not only in Japanese painting but in all of art.
Yoritomo (1147–99) was the founder of the house of Minamoto,
the organizer of the palace stewardship (Baku-fu), and belonged
to a military regime which had its seat in the new capital of
Kamakura. Yoritomo is portrayed seated in the ceremonial dress
(Sokutai) of a senior court official. His pale face rises like a sharp
accent above the angularly defined black figure and pale lines
98 delineate nose and eyes above a full mouth.

Attributed to FUJIWARA NOBUZANE (1176–1265) *The Poetess Ko-ogimi* (detail) · 13th century · India ink and color on paper · $14\frac{1}{8} \times 23\frac{1}{4}''$ · Yamato Bunka-kan Museum, Nara

The poetess Ko-ogimi, better known as Kodai-no-kimi, numbers among the thirty-six poets and poetesses considered as the classical writers of the Heian period and profoundly admired in Japan for many centuries. This picture belonged originally to a series of thirty-six portraits of poets in two hand scrolls which were cut up a few years ago and are now scattered among several collections. The artist Fujiwara Nobuzane was one of Takanobu's sons and shares his father's fame as a portraitist. More than a portrait of a person we see here an extravagant profusion of magnificent robes such as the women of those times wore layer over layer, as many as twenty-five at a time. The gradation of colors evident on the sleeves and borders was an expression of the taste and culture of the wearer. Fine locks of long black hair frame her white-powdered face with its blackened teeth and high-arched eyebrows. There is here a symphony of colors which almost obscures the figure and yet forms a charming frame for the face.

99

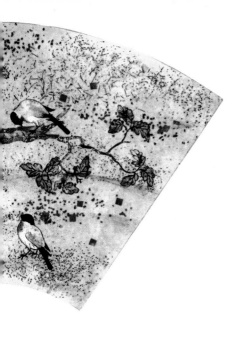

Leaf of a fan from the Hokkekyo Sutra · 12th century · India ink,
color, gold, and silver on paper · $10\frac{1}{8} \times 19\frac{3}{8}''$ · Fujita Museum,
Osaka

Late in the Heian period a series of decorative copies of the
Hokkekyo Sutra appeared (the Sutra of the Lotus of the Good
Doctrine, compare also page 93), which were done by noble
ladies and gentlemen. Of these copies a great many are painted
and written on fans, some of which still exist in various collections.
This fan-shaped album leaf with a gnarled tree, birds, and
bamboo on paper sprinkled with gold and silver and spots of
cut-out gold leaf *(kirikane)* has a sumptuous effect and is techni-
cally interesting: the contours were printed from a woodblock,
while the strong colors were painted in by hand. The text of the
Sutra is on the reverse side of the leaf.

EN-I *The Priest Ippen on a Journey* (detail) · 1299 · India ink and
pale color on silk · Total dimensions of scroll, $14\frac{7}{8} \times 427\frac{1}{4}''$ ·
Kankiko-ji, Kyoto

As early as ten years after his death, the life of the wandering
priest Ippen (1239–89) was portrayed by the artist En-i in twelve
scrolls. The biographical text that accompanies the pictorial
scrolls is the work of the priest Shokei, and it is likely that En-
i was also a monk. Several versions of the biography of Ippen
(Ippen-Shonin-Eden) have been preserved in Japan, but the 1299
version by En-i is probably the most important. Ippen was one
of the most outstanding wandering priests, a missionary for the
Nembutsu movement (the invocation of the Amida Buddha
"Namu Amida Butsu"). For many years he traveled through all
parts of Japan winning numerous disciples. Here he is journeying
to Dazaifu on the southern island of Kyushu with his pupil
Shokei in search of his instructor. Ippen and Shokei are dressed
simply and carry umbrellas; they are followed by three monks
and two luggage-bearers. Well-balanced, vigorous lines delineate
the contours of the promontory, on the far side of which dark
pines rise up from the cliffs and a flock of birds flies over the
water. Even if we know nothing of the artist, he must surely be
counted among the leading early landscape painters of Japan.

GYOGEN (documented 1286–1300) *Shinto Goddess* · Dated 1295 ·
Paint on panel · $75\frac{5}{8} \times 20\frac{1}{8}''$ · Yakushi-ji, Nara

Gyogen was a Buddhist painter who belonged to the workshop
of a temple *(e-dokoro)* in Nara which was set up to replace older
and, by that time, damaged paintings done around 1087. These
religious paintings frequently depict a mixture of Shinto and
Buddhist deities. The Shinto gods of Yakushi-ji are mostly
dignified figures in the ceremonial costume of high court officials
(Sokutai). The goddesses, as this example illustrates, were
portrayed as voluptuous beauties with pleasing faces, wearing
crowns and long-sleeved decorative robes in accordance with the
aesthetic ideal and the fashions of the Chinese T'ang dynasty.

The Nachi Waterfall · c. 1300 · India ink and color on silk · $62\frac{3}{4}$ × $22\frac{3}{4}''$ · Nezu Museum, Tokyo

This grandiose view of the Nachi Waterfall is not just a landscape; it is at the same time a religious painting symbolizing the deity of this waterfall, even if the deity himself is not portrayed. During the Kamakura period many pictures of Shinto shrines in their natural environment *(Mandara)* were produced, pictures in which the landscape increasingly supplanted the shrine and became the actual subject. At the end of that development is this painting of the Nachi Waterfall, the fundamental idea of which is still rooted in the religious worship of nature practiced by the Japanese, as is indicated by the golden semiorb of sun visible over the mountains. The force of the waterfall plunging steeply downward is stressed by the dazzling whiteness, beside which the structure of the rocks recedes and only the bluish green of the pines stands out.

MINCHO (1352–1431) *Ten Rakan* · Dated 1386 · India ink and color on silk · 68⅛ × 35⅜″ · Nezu Museum, Tokyo

In the fourteenth century, relations with China once again became close, particularly in the monasteries of the Zen Buddhists, and the style of the Chinese ink painting of the Southern Sung Academy was enthusiastically taken up by Japanese artists. Mincho, known also as Chodensu because of his priestly office, was a monk in the Zen monastery of Tofuku-ji in Kyoto. He produced pure ink paintings in the style of the Southern Sung Academy and became famous for his colorful portraits of Buddhist saints. In 1386 he created a series of fifty paintings portraying the 500 Rakan (pupils of Buddha). These are closely derived from Chinese prototypes of the same period. This picture is from that series, which is still preserved almost complete in Tofuku-ji. The colorful robes of the disciples of Buddha form a strong contrast to the delicate mountainous landscape and clouds of the background. Mincho was the first artist to adapt themes from Zen Buddhism, and his works repeatedly reveal the technique of a professional painter.

SOGA JASOKU (documented 1452–83) *Daruma* · India ink and pale color on paper · $26\frac{3}{8} \times 15\frac{3}{4}''$ · Yotoku-in, Kyoto

Jasoku came from Echizen, lived in Kyoto, and belonged to the Samurai class. He was the pupil of the artist and monk Shubun who was celebrated for his ink paintings in the Sung style. The portrayal of Daruma (Bodhidarma), the first patriarch of Chinese Ch'an (Japanese Zen) Buddhism, was a favorite motif of Japanese Zen painting in the fifteenth century. Once, according to legend, Daruma's eyes closed while he was in meditation, and in his fury he ripped off his eyelids. He is consequently portrayed with large eyes (in fact, lidless), which dominate his face, and a red cloak drawn over his head covers his body and hands.

KEI SHOKI (documented 1478–1523) *Landscape* · Leaf of a fan ·
India ink and pale colors on paper · $13\frac{1}{4} \times 14\frac{1}{8}''$ · Museum for
Eastern Asiatic Art, Cologne

Kei Shoki (Shokei) was a priest at Kencho-ji in Kamakura where
he held the office of scribe *(Shoki)*. In 1478 he traveled to Kyoto,
remained there three years as a pupil of the famous painter
Geiami (1431–85), and then returned to Kamakura with its many
Zen monasteries. The small leaf of a fan, mounted as a hanging
scroll, shows that Kei Shoki was accomplished in the art of
classical Chinese landscape painting. The crags on the right,
which seem to be hewn by an ax, and the wiry trees are in the
best Sung tradition of Ma Yuan and Hsai Kuei. The soft green
of the leaves and pine needles, the fading blue of the distant
mountains between the cloud banks, and the touch of red in the
servant's hat to intensify all the other colors prove Kei Shoki to
be a lyrical composer in color.

Portrait of Sogi · 16th century · India ink and color on silk
41 × 16¾″ · Collection Nambu, Tokyo

The monk Sogi (1421–1502) was a well-known poet who had a
great love of nature and wandered widely throughout the country. He is particularly famous for his series of poems (Renga),
which he brought out as a collection in 1495. Sogi is portrayed
seated and dressed in the violet, black, and brown habit of a
priest; his finely featured head stands out above the white undergarment. The face is shaped by delicate lines. The accentuated
brows above his lively eyes and the fine flourish of his mouth
make this the portrait of a dignified, sensitive man.

Attributed to HASEGAWA KYUZO (1568–93) *Cherry Blossoms* ·
Sliding doors · Color, India ink, and gold on paper · Height,
69½″ · Chishaku-in Monastery, Kyoto

The four sliding doors, two of which are illustrated here, belonged
originally to the Shoun-ji temple which was erected by Hideyoshi
in 1591 to the memory of his deceased favorite son; they came
into the hands of the Chishaku Monastery at a later date. These
doors have often been attributed to Hasegawa Tohaku, the
father of Kyuzo, whose pair of screens in a similar style still
exist. But the *Cherry Blossoms* panels are definitely the work of
another hand, being more delicate in conception and less emphatic
in their realization. It is quite possible, however, that the young
Kyuzo helped his father with the Shoun-ji screens and that these
doors were painted in collaboration with him. While one can
sense the influence of Eitoku, what is lacking here is the courage to
tackle large forms. The blossoms are finely detailed, painted in
gouache, and stand out from the gold background as if in relief. 111

KANO EITOKU (1543–90) *Pine Trees and Eagle* · Screen · India ink, color, and gold on paper · $63\frac{1}{4} \times 138''$ · Academy of Art, Tokyo

Kano Eitoku was a grandson and probably also a pupil of Kano Motonobu (1476–1559); he was court painter to the most powerful men of his time, Oda Nobunag and Toyotomi Hideyoshi, who had their new palaces decorated in splendor but without pretension. Eitoku evolved a style which made it possible to cover large spaces decoratively. Many screens and sliding doors were painted by him, but only a few that can be attributed to him with any certainty have been preserved. Among these is the pair of screens with pine trees and eagles—this one among them— which were attributed to Eitoku by Kano Eino, one of his great-grandsons. As with all the existing works, this is unsigned, but it shows all those features for which Eitoku was famous. He links the brilliant blue and green of the Yamato-e—the Kitano-Tenjin scroll (page 97)—with the vigorous brush strokes of the Kano school. The decorative background of clouds in dull-finished gold leaf gives the colors even greater luminosity.   113

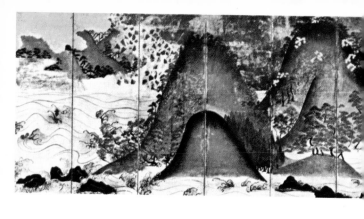

The Four Seasons · 16th century · Pair of screens · Color, India ink, and gold on paper · Each 58⅝ × 124″ · Kongo-ji, Osaka

The method of composition of the Yamato-e scrolls is applied here to screens. The passing of the seasons from spring to summer, then to autumn and winter, is depicted on two six-sectioned screens. There is a bold use of color: green and blue on a gold base in the summer screen, and for autumn and winter extraordinarily cold colors such as brown, green, white, and dark blue, and then the entire surface sprinkled with gold and silver. The mountains rise disk-shaped behind one another, while extremely clever brushwork is displayed in the waves and tree trunks. Such boldness of composition and coloring does not appear again until the art of Sotatsu.

KANO SANRAKU (1559–1635) *The Three Laughing Men of the Valley of the Tiger* · Screen · Color, India ink, and gold on paper · National Museum, Tokyo

Kano Sanraku came from Omi and was the son of the painter Kimura Nagamitsu. He studied under Kano Eitoku in Kyoto and worked for Hideyoshi. The latter esteemed the young painter so highly that Eitoku adopted him. Sanraku later became his son-in-law and successor as head of the Kano school in Kyoto. There are some magnificent ink paintings by Sanraku and equally decorative works on screens and doors. Here he takes up the theme of a Chinese legend: a hermit in the Valley of the Tiger had made up his mind never again to cross the small bridge; one day, accompanying two friends with whom he was deep in conversation, he crossed the bridge without noticing it. When they realized what had happened they all three roared with laughter. The landscape with its strong colors still preserves the energy of Eitoku, even if the latter's masterly freedom in covering large surfaces has given way here to a more subtle draftsmanship in individual shapes.

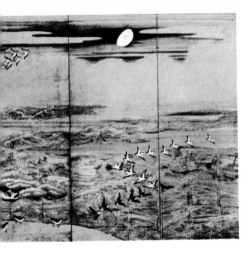

KANO SANSETSU (1589–1651) *Seabirds on a Winter Coast* · Screen ·
Color, India ink, and gold on paper · 61 × 143¼″ · Collection
Hosotsugi, Kyoto

Kano Sansetsu was the pupil of his father-in-law Kano Sanraku,
whose name he took, as was usual in cases of adoption. He came
from Hizen, lived in Kyoto, and inherited the leadership of the
Kano school in Kyoto from his master after many members of
the painter's family had drifted away to the new capital Edo
(Tokyo). It is difficult to distinguish the works of Sanraku from
those of Sansetsu, and opinions differ, especially with regard to
screens and sliding doors, most of which are unsigned. The pair
of screens with waterfowl—one of which is illustrated here—
belong to those works which have been attributed with some
certainty to Sansetsu. Sansetsu combines asymmetrical composition and highly skillful, finely detailed draftsmanship with
decorative brilliance, elements similar to those we find also in
the applied arts of the time.

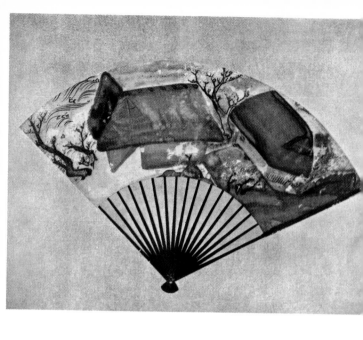

Attributed to TAWARAYA SOTATSU (early 17th century) · Picture
constructed with fans · Color, India ink, and gold on paper ·
Height, 7″ · Sambo-in, Kyoto

Very little is known of Sotatsu's life; the only certain dates are
1602 and 1630. He was a friend of Koetsu (1558–1637), the
greatest calligrapher of his day, and worked in collaboration
with him. According to tradition he is reputed to have been a
painter of fans by profession. The exceptionally free composition
of the straw-covered farmhouses in the semicircle of the fan seen
here demonstrates his unusual gift for composition. Consider
too the sensitive use of cold colors which gives the picture a
painterly charm. This fan is part of a two-sectioned gold-backed
screen on which the fans have been newly mounted. Because the
screen is in the possession of the Sambo-in in the Daigo-ji
temple, where Sotatsu lived for some time, one can consider it
his work with certainty, even though the individual fans are
unsigned.

Attributed to TAWARAYA SOTATSU *Ise Monogatari, Akutagawa* ·
Leaf of an album · India ink, color, and gold on paper · $9\frac{5}{8}$ ×
$8\frac{1}{4}''$ · Yamato Bunka-kan Museum, Nara

It was not only in his use of color that Sotatsu returned to the
tradition of Yamato-e painting, for he also took as models the
classical narrative pictures of the tenth, eleventh, and twelfth
centuries and, indeed, "copied" them, although in his own
individual style. His great achievement lies firstly in his revival
of Yamato-e art and secondly in his treatment of color, which he
used in the same way as India ink. He was thus able to depict
classical themes in a highly decorative manner, even on large
surfaces. This small leaf from the tenth-century tale of *Ise
Monogatari* shows Prince Narihara carrying a beautiful lady
across dewy fields by the river Akutagawa. With great skill the
artist paints strongly colored areas over a gold background and
integrates the written text into the composition.

OGATA KORIN (1658–1716) *Irises* · Screen · Color on gold-ground paper · $59\frac{5}{8} \times 141\frac{1}{4}''$ · Nezu Museum, Tokyo

Ogata Korin, son of a kimono manufacturer in Kyoto, was related to Koetsu and consequently from an early age was familiar with painting. His family's wealth made it possible for him to live freely as an artist. Even during his lifetime his artworks, whether in lacquer, ceramics, silk, India ink, or gold, were valued most highly, and craftsmen of all kinds adopted his forms as models. In a pair of screens painted with irises—only one is illustrated here—he achieved one of his most beautiful decorative works. The motif, taken from the *Ise Monogatari*, can also be found in his lacquer work. It comes from the "Yatsubashi" Chapter (the Eightfold Bridge) in which the hero Narihara writes a poem about the irises alongside the Yatsubashi bridge (a bridge made out of eight simple planks placed together to form a zigzag leading across the marsh). There is neither water nor bridge on this screen, but the thick clumps of iris, with the full splendor of their blooms, suffice to awaken the memory of this poem. With simple means—flat unshaded green juxtaposed with lapis lazuli on a shimmering gold ground—Korin was able to achieve a superb decorative effect.

Genre Scene · 17th century · Detail from a pair of four-sectioned screens · India ink, color, gold, and silver on paper

A series of screens portraying scenes from everyday life has been preserved from the seventeenth century, the beginning of the Edo period. Such themes, however, were not considered worthy to be treated in painting, and these works are unsigned because the authors did not wish to risk their reputations. Customers for such "glimpses of this transitory world" (Ukiyo-e) were to be found among the wealthy upper middle classes, which, particularly in Edo (Tokyo), were coming to exert considerable influence on artistic activity and whose ideals were focused on the pleasures of this world. This detail portrays men and women of no particular distinction, dressed simply and carrying on in a most relaxed manner. The artist lavished special care on the patterns of the clothing and caught on paper the wealth of color characteristic of Japanese fashions. To these he added gold leaf and sprinkled silver to give an impression of luxuriousness.

HISHIKAWA MORONOBU (d. 1694) *Beauty with Attendant* · India ink and color on paper

Hishikawa Moronobu was the first artist to turn out Ukiyo-e pictures in the exacting form suited to the woodcut. He lived in Edo and was a tapestry worker by profession. It is not known whether he was ever the pupil of any established painter or whether he belonged to some workshop. In his work, which does not only portray beautiful women, we are reminded of the styles of both the Yamato-e and the Kano school. He created a large number of book illustrations for a public that found its entertainment in popular literature. Besides these, he also painted pictures of the beautiful women of Yoshiwara, the red-light district of Edo.

MIYAGAWA CHOSHUN (1682–1752) *A Beauty* (detail) · India ink
and color on silk · Total dimensions, $44\frac{1}{8} \times 23\frac{1}{2}''$

Miyagawa Choshun came from Owari, went to Edo, and there
became one of Moronobu's best pupils. The beautiful woman
here fanning herself to keep cool is one of Choshun's classical
works. The design on her kimono is evidence of Choshun's
pronounced sense of color. The main tone is a subdued brownish
red against which gleams the white of the chrysanthemums. Black
tresses of hair tumble in a gentle rhythm round her head, which
is inclined to one side; her white-powdered face stands out
above the red of the collar, while strong regular lines mark the
folds and contours of her robe.

Torii Kiyonobu I (1664–1728) *Pantomime* · c. 1726 · India ink and color on paper · 13 × 17″ · Collection Kuwahara

Torii Kiyonobu I came to Edo in 1687 with his father, an actor who also painted posters for the theater. In the same year his first book illustrations appeared, modeled after those of Moronobu. His intimate contact with the theater made him the first artist in that genre: he painted large-scale portraits of actors as well as scenery and posters to be reproduced in woodcuts, a medium which began to be used in 1695. This small picture draws its subject from the theater, depicting a dancer in the "Tsuri Kitsune" pantomime. Disguised as a man, a fox who has been ravaging the area dances around the trap a farmer has set. While the fox-man urges the farmer to destroy the snare, the scent of the bait—a roasted rat—is wafted to his nose and, unable to resist, his disguise is revealed, and he is caught by the farmer. With few but forceful lines Kiyonobu delineates the dancer, and the lively movement is emphasized by the bright colors of the costume. 127

KATSUKAWA SHUNSHO (1726–96) *April* and *August* · India ink and color on silk · Height, 40¼″ · Collection Nakano, Niigata

Katsukawa Shunsho is doubly famous as a Ukiyo-e painter and as a woodcut designer. He was a pupil of Miyagawa Choshun, whose influence can still be traced in Shunsho's portraits of women. These two narrow pictures belong to a series of ten (formerly twelve) paintings of the months in which the customs of their festivals are represented by beautiful women. April (the third moon) is the time to admire the cherry blossom and to play a kind of football: here the ball has got caught in the tree, and the ladies are trying to dislodge it with a small stick. In August (the seventh moon) the Tanabata festival is celebrated, where the Heavenly Weaver and the Shepherd, the two constellations that meet only once a year in the Milky Way, are honored. For the occasion, small strips of paper with poems are hung from the trees. The artist had a masterly comprehension of how to arrange his colors and figures in this narrow format, and these paintings certainly have their place among Shunsho's most significant works.

KAIGETSUDO ANDO (c. 1700) *Courtesan and Maid* · c. 1713 · India
ink and color on paper · $38\frac{5}{8} \times 17\frac{1}{2}''$ · Collection Takeoka

Kaigetsudo Ando was the leader of the Kaigetsudo group. It
was Ando who created the type of large figure with sharp contours and broad flat areas of kimono decorated with a diversity of
patterns typical of the fashions of the time. This picture of a
courtesan with her servant is considered one of Kaigetsudo
Ando's best works. The delicacy of color in the robes is achieved
by applying wet paint over a moist surface, and the details of the
pattern can be made out in the wide expanse of the sleeves and
borders. The splendid kimono seems to be the real subject of
the painting more than its gracious wearer herself.

Ko Sukoku (1730–1804) *Yorimasa Slays a Monster* · Dated 1787 ·
Paint on wood · 116⅞ × 147⅞″ · Senso-ji, Tokyo

Sukoku lived in Edo and was a pupil of the well-known Hanabusa
Itcho; he later studied Yamato-e painting, the techniques of
which he applied to his genre paintings and, above all, to the
historical pictures for which he became especially famous. He
was particularly apt in historical paintings with several figures,
as this picture shows. With the help of his attendant Inohayata,
Yorimasa—one of the heroes of Japanese mythology and often
portrayed as the hero in plays—is slaying a monster which has
been prowling round the Emperor's palace. Energetic brushwork
together with finely detailed patches of color are the outstanding
characteristics of this picture. The fierce expression of the hero
and the violence of the depiction may have prepared the way for
Kuniyoshi, one of the later masters of the Japanese woodcut. 131

MARUYAMA OKYO (1733–95) *Wild Geese* · Dated 1767 · India ink and color on paper · $58\frac{1}{4} \times 54\frac{3}{4}''$ · Emman-in, Otsu

In the eighteenth century, under the influence of Europe and China, there occurred an outburst of realism in Japanese art, and Maruyama Okyo is rightly regarded as its most important exponent. From European copperplate engravings he studied vanishing-point perspective, and from the work of the Chinese painter Shen Nan-p'in, who was also under European influence, he learned to depict animals and plants realistically. This painting of wild geese over the sea is one of the best examples from which to understand his conceptions: the diverse movements of the geese are brilliantly observed and set down, and the use of color is true to nature and full of life; yet this is saved from being a mere nature study by virtue of the skillful composition. The energetic drawing of the waves demonstrates the classical tradition of Okyo's painting, and the bright red foliage, forming a stark contrast to the rocks and birds, reveals his sense of decorative values.

NAGASAWA ROSETSU (1754–99) *Yamauba and Kintoki* · India ink, color, and gold on silk · 66 × 33¼″ · Itsukushima-jinja, Akino-kuni

Rosetsu lived in Kyoto and was probably the most original pupil of Maruyama Okyo. In his paintings, the realism of his master is softened by wit and humor, as in this depiction of Yamauba with Kintoki. Mountain witch and foster mother of the boy-hero Kintoki who has the strength of a bear, Yamauba is portrayed in splendid but somewhat tattered garments, with a torn parasol and the furrowed face of an old crone. With her left hand she clutches Kintoki, who is generally painted red as a symbol of his extraordinary physical strength.

YAMAGUCHI SOKEN (1759–1818) *Young Woman under a Pine Tree* ·
India ink and color on silk

Like Rosetsu, Yamaguchi Soken was a pupil of Okyo and lived
in Kyoto. He is famous particularly as a painter of beautiful
women. The young woman standing under a pine tree justifies
this reputation. Her posture and movement are full of natural
charm. Her right hand points into the distance while with a
bamboo switch in her left hand she gathers mushrooms. The
rhythm of the patterned *obi* (sash) corresponds to the curve of her
body. The violet kimono with its red undergarment and white
collar stands out in strong contrast against the lightly shaded
background, and all this makes the small face seem all the more
animated.

SAKAI HOITSU (1761–1828) *Summer Grass in the Rain* · Wall
screen in two folds · India ink, color, and gold on silver-ground
paper · $55\frac{1}{8} \times 72''$ · Commission for Protection of Cultural
Properties of Japan, Tokyo

Hoitsu is regarded as the last great artist of the Sotatsu-Korin
school, although there is evidence in his pictures of the realism
which Okyo had introduced into Japanese art. In the pair of
screens called *Summer Grass in the Rain* and *Antumn Grass in the
Wind* (the former is illustrated here), he paints grass and flowers
very accurately and naturalistically, catching the way they bend
heavily under the rain. Across the upper right corner of the screen
meanders a dark blue stream with golden waves, while the red
and white of the flowers on the dull silver background give the
picture a lively brilliance. This pair of screens makes up the reverse
side to Korin's celebrated pair with the gods of thunder and of
wind, the summer grass in the rain corresponding to the god
of thunder. While this example of Hoitsu's work is decorative in
effect, it lacks the broad sweeping mastery with which Korin or
Sotatsu fills large surfaces.

URAGAMI GYOKUDO (1745–1820) *Autumn Landscape* · Leaf of an album · India ink and pale color on paper · $11\frac{3}{8} \times 8\frac{7}{8}''$ · Collection Umezawa, Tokyo

Gyokudo was a Samurai in the service of the Ikeda family in the province of Bizen. His love of music made him quit that service after forty-nine years, in order to be free to wander around the country with his *koto*, a kind of thirteen-stringed zither. Later he began to paint in a free and very unconventional style which recalls the seventeenth-century "Individualists" in China. With short strokes of an almost dry brush, he sketches in the hill in the background, and for the trees and rocks of the foreground he makes the separate strokes firmer and heavier. The patches of undergrowth are freely distributed, as are the yellow and red of the autumn foliage. It is understandable that Gyokudo's work was received with enthusiasm in Europe, however much it may differ from our Western way of looking at things.

YOSA BUSON (1716–83) *Autumn Landscape* (detail) · Dated 1780 ·
Sliding door · India ink and pale color on silk laid on gold ·
13 × 17⅛″ · Museum for Eastern Asiatic Art, Cologne

Together with Gyokudo, Buson was one of the most important
exponents of the stylistic tendency called in Japan *Bunjin-gwa*
(in Chinese, *Wen-jen-hua*, "literary painting," whose foremost
exponent around 1600 was Tung Ch'i-ch'ang, see page 54). Its
enthusiastic reception by a great many artists was due to the fact
that this subjective landscape painting allowed the individual
artist greater freedom than the traditional schools. This sliding
door of a small wall cupboard is the third in a series of four: the
four sections making up a single landscape were designed to
hang like hand scrolls over four doors. In the foreground is a
group of rocks with gnarled trees; a path leads past them to
Chinese-style peasant dwellings huddled together in a village.
The touches of blue on some of the rocks and the russet of the
foliage stand out delicately against the dull shimmer of the gold
background.

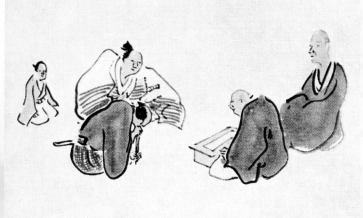

YOSA BUSON *The Narrow Path into the Back Country* (detail) · Dated
1778 · Hand scroll · India ink and pale color on paper · Height,
11⅜" · Nagao Museum, Tokyo

Buson was not only an important painter but also a *Haiku* poet
of some fame (*Haiku* are short poems of seventeen syllables). He
came from a small community near Osaka and in 1737 moved with
his family to Edo where he became a pupil of Hayano Bajin
(1677–1742), the *Haiku* poet. In this period, his main interest was
probably in poetry. After his master's death, he wandered
through Japan, visited friends, and eagerly acquainted himself
with Chinese painting. Along with the *Bunjin-gwa* style of painting,
he practiced another style, one which was related to his poetry.
This was *Haigwa*, concise short poems illustrated in painting.
The present picture, one of his best-known works, belongs to
this tendency. Buson here depicts the wanderings of Basho, the
most famous of the Japanese *Haiku* poets. With short, pregnant
brush strokes and discreet colors he portrays the various phases
138 of the journey with wit and poetry.

AOKI MOKUBEI (1767–1833) *Morning Sun over Uji* · Dated 1824 ·
India ink and pale color on paper · 19⅝ × 31¾″ · Commission for
Protection of Cultural Properties of Japan, Tokyo

Like Buson in his later years, Mokubei lived in Kyoto and was
a pupil of Ike-no Taiga (1723–76). He is perhaps the last great
master of literary painting *(Bunjin-gwa)*, and he lived well into the
nineteenth century. In addition to his other talents, he was a
famous amateur potter. Like many intellectuals of his time, he
was very interested in the art and literature of China and learned
much from the paintings of the Ming and early Ch'ang dynasties
(sixteenth and seventeenth centuries). His paintings are characterized by their cool colors and a feeling for spatial depth. They
are quite comparable to the works of his master Taiga, even if
they do not perhaps have the spontaneity which is the special
charm of Buson's work. The picture seen here is justifiably
regarded as one of his most important paintings. It is more a
pictorial conception of an ideal landscape than a realistic portrait
of some particular place, and it is executed with lovely brushwork
and dots of color introduced here and there as accents. 139

Utagawa Kuniyoshi (1798–1861) *Young Woman* · c. 1855 ·
India ink and pale color on silk · $36\frac{5}{8} \times 13\frac{1}{4}''$ · Museum for
Eastern Asiatic Art, Cologne

Born in Tokyo, Kuniyoshi was the son of a silk-dyer. At the age
of thirteen he came under the instruction of Toyokuni, then the
most popular master of the woodcut on theatrical subjects. At
nineteen he was already an independent artist famous for his
paintings of heroes and battles. His woodcuts with their energetic
use of color were highly appreciated and sought after in the
nineteenth century when they first came to Europe, but today
are somewhat looked down upon as crude and garish, though
they are full of expressive dramatic qualities in composition. Be
that as it may, this picture of a young woman is restrained in
color. The twist of the head, however, with the hair ruffled by
the wind, still shows something of the painter's expressive
vitality. Although elsewhere he is lavish in his use of powerful
accents of color, here he makes do with a light red for the undergarment and black for the collar and sandal straps to create a
carefully balanced color composition.   141

SHIBATA ZESSHIN (1807–91) *Blossoming Branches and Bamboos* ·
Leaf of an album · Lacquer on paper · $7\frac{1}{4} \times 6\frac{3}{8}''$ · Herbig-Haar-
haus Lacquer Museum, Cologne

Shibata Zesshin was the last great artist working with lacquer.
Determined to free himself from the standardized designs for
lacquer furnished by the painters and woodcut artists, he went to
Kyoto in 1825 to study painting for himself under various
masters. This picture is taken from an album with five leaves
which were all painted on paper in lacquer colors. Bold in composition and subtle in execution, it achieves a decorative effect,
which is further emphasized by the bright colors laid over the
142 delicate gold bands of cloud.

KATSUSHIKA HOKUSAI (1760–1849) *Duck with Watermelon* ·
1847 · Leaf of an album · India ink and color on silk · Collection
Sakata, Tokyo

Due to his innumerable woodcuts, Hokusai is probably the
Japanese artist best known to the West. There, no less than in
the East, he has been much written about. But Hokusai the
painter is less known, although rich material is in existence and
he was hardly less productive as a painter than as a woodcut
designer. His work is so extensive that, even though it was the
product of a long life, one can hardly imagine it to have come
from the hand of a single painter. This small leaf, painted at the
age of eighty-seven, is a good example of his self-confident gift of
imagination. The duck is captured in its natural movement on
the water, its plumage is painted with great subtlety, while the
slice of melon like a sickle-moon echoes the pattern of the waves. 143

YOKOYAMA TAIKWAN (1868–1958) *Red Maple* · Dated 1931 ·
Screen · India ink, color, gold, and silver on paper · $63\frac{3}{4} \times 142\frac{5}{8}''$
· Private collection, Japan

Taikwan lived in Tokyo and is regarded as one of the leading
figures among modern Japanese artists. He was a pupil of
Hashimoto Gaho (1835–1908) and Kakuzo Okakura. The latter
founded the School of Art in Tokyo and together with the
American Ernest Fenollosa did a great deal toward preservation
of Japanese works of art of the past at a time when Japan was
plunging headlong and with enormous enthusiasm into the
new culture of the West. Taikwan, who worked right through
his old age, was firmly opposed to all innovations and practiced
and handed on the traditional forms. The pair of screens in six
sections depicting red maple trees (only one reproduced here)
shows for all its naturalism (reminiscent of Maruyama Okyo) a
decorative brilliance whose effect is made by the use of gleaming
colors. This screen follows the best tradition of the late sixteenth
century, the Momoyama period.

YOKOYAMA TAIKWAN *Fujiyama at Dawn* · 1955 · India ink, pale
color, and gold on silk · 17¾ × 22½″ · Museum for Eastern
Asiatic Art, Cologne

If the screen done by Taikwan in 1931 (pages 144/45) is in the
tradition of the late sixteenth century, here the artist expresses the
opposite side of his personality and of Japanese art by his masterly
use of ink. The radiant whiteness of Fujiyama rises up over
clouds and pine trees in the golden light of sunrise. Taikwan is
regarded as one of the greatest masters of India-ink technique in
the twentieth century, and if one examines the finely shaded tones
of the trees and clouds one understands why he has enjoyed such
146 high esteem in Japan.

TOMIOKA TESSAI (1836–1924) *Journey to the Red Wall* (detail) ·
India ink and color on paper · Total dimensions, $61\frac{3}{8} \times 16\frac{7}{8}''$ ·
Kiyoshi-Kojin Temple

The Journey to the Red Wall, based on the prose poem of Su
Tung-p'o (1036–1101), is a recurrent theme in Chinese painting.
During his exile the poet often sailed to these cliffs in his boat to
meditate on the naval battle that had taken place there in A.D.
208. Here Tessai portrays one of Su Tung-p'o's expeditions:
with his friends he stands on the shore, accompanied by a servant
with food for a picnic slung over his shoulder in two hampers.
The artist has captured this cheerful gathering with lively colors
and boldly powerful brushwork.

ISHIKAWA BIHO (1902–   ) *Walk in the Fields in Autumn* ·
Screen in two sections · India ink and color on paper

Biho is one of the modern Ukiyoe painters who have taken the
masters of the early seventeenth century as models. With sharply
defined contours the figures are placed prominently in the foreground. Their colorful kimonos stand out decoratively against
the background of autumn plants and bright maple leaves. As
in the early Ukiyoe paintings, the dark hair forms a severe frame
around the white faces and also creates a lively contrast of colors.
The outlines and folds of the garments are clearly and finely
drawn without any particular emphasis. This pair of screens, one
of which is illustrated here, demonstrates how the finest aspects
148 of the Japanese tradition live on in the painting of today.

INDEX

ACKNOWLEDGMENTS

The publisher and the author express their gratitude and appreci-
ation to all the museums, galleries, cultural authorities, and
private collectors who so graciously made available for this book
the works in their custody or possession. All such sources are
acknowledged in the captions for the individual reproductions.

YOU'RE RUNNING THE PROGRAM!

A burning temple . . .
A tossing ship . . .
A royal palace . . .
An underground hideout . . .

Where are you? And, more importantly, what **time** is it?

It's hard to say what country or what century you've landed in when you travel in Professor Q's time machine. But one thing is always true: only by using your wits will you ever get back to the twentieth century. . . .

Where you go and what happens to you will depend on the choices you make. There are 28 possible endings! And it all starts with what you do on a lazy day off from school. . . .

PROFESSOR Q'S
MYSTERIOUS MACHINE

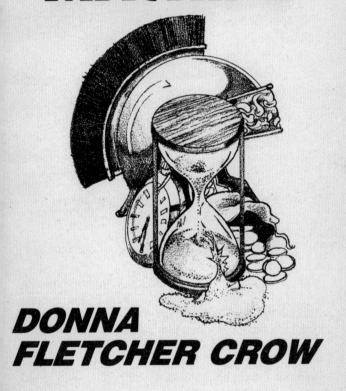

DONNA
FLETCHER CROW

Chariot Books

For Stanley, Preston, and John

PROFESSOR Q'S MYSTERIOUS MACHINE
© 1982 Donna Fletcher Crow for text and Kurt Mitchell for
illustrations.
Book and series design by Ray Cioni/The Cioni Artworks.

Printed in the United States of America.

ISBN: 0-89191-562-1
LC: 82-71336

CAUTION!

This is not a normal book! If you read it straight through, it won't make sense.

Instead, you must start at page 1 and then turn to the pages where your choices lead you. Your first situation — what to do on a day off from school — is one you've made fairly often. But after that, your decisions can lead you to other times and places — and if you're not careful, you'll never get back!

If you want to read this book, you must choose to **Turn to page 1.**

Today you had only a half day of school. Teachers have some kind of meeting or something. A whole afternoon to yourself! You wander out into your backyard and wonder what to do.

"Hi! What're you doing?" Your friend Chris strolls through the gate.

"Nothing."

"Want to go with me to visit Professor Quinten?"

"Professor who?"

"Quinten. I've told you about him lots of times. You know: he went to college with my folks, and he invents things. My dad borrowed this book from him and I'm going to return it."

You peer at the title. "**Instantaneity Synchronization**. What's that?"

"Dad said it was about time, sort of. I don't really know. Are you coming?"

You shrug and get to your feet. Why not?

It's about a half mile walk to the professor's place. The man's house isn't at all what you expect. It's a little white cottage with pink roses growing around it. Good grief!

When he doesn't answer the doorbell after the third ring, you feel almost relieved.

Then you hear footsteps on the other side of the door. The door opens slowly and you look up — all the way up. Past his scuffed brown shoes, up his rumpled, stained, baggy plaid pants, about five feet of them, up his dusty pink shirt that's buttoned wrong, up his long, skinny neck, up his long, skinny face, up to his thick black hair sticking out in all directions.

Chris knows what to expect, so he isn't the least bit shocked. "Hi, Professor Quinten. Dad asked me to bring this book back."

"How nice. Won't you come in? And please, call me Professor Q." His voice sounds normal.

The room you step into isn't at all like the cozy exterior of the house. It seems to be a laboratory of some kind. A computer bank lines one wall of the room, and drafting tables stand in rows on the other side, each with complicated drawings on top.

Professor Quinten leads you and Chris to an object sitting in the back of the room under an opening in the roof. He points to the object with obvious pride.

You peer at the gleaming, silvery white thing, trying to think of a way to describe it. A giant, elongated, lumpy egg? A fat, metal cigar? A blimp standing on end?

Professor Q starts to say something when the phone rings. He looks around as if trying to figure out what's making such a strange noise. Then he gives a short nod and disappears through a doorway, around a corner, and down a hall.

"What do you suppose that thing is?" You nudge Chris, who walks around the contraption.

"Hey, here's a door. Come on. Wow, look at this!" Chris steps inside.

Choices: You wait for Professor Q to come back (turn to page 16).
You get in (turn to page 3).

You duck inside the mysterious silver object, feeling rather guilty, but excited, too. There are two seats inside it.

"Hey, look, another computer!" Chris says. "Have you ever seen the games you can play on these things? In math class we—"

"Don't touch anything!" You're worrying about what the professor will say if he comes back and finds you in his invention, whatever it is.

All of a sudden the machine begins to vibrate. It jerks. Then it shakes. You're thrown back into one of the seats.

"What did you do? I said not to touch anything!" you yell.

Chris looks as pale as a ghost. You should have known better than to let him near anything electronic.

The machine goes on vibrating, then gives a last shudder, and all is still.

You take a deep breath. You'd been holding your breath all that time. "Chris, are you crazy? You could have broken something!"

"Well, doesn't look like I did."

"Let's get out," you say and grab the door handle. "I hope the professor hasn't—"

You don't get to finish your sentence. You are grabbed by a pair of huge, burly hands and pulled roughly out the door. You blink to get used to the bright light outside, then look up into angry black eyes and a bushy black beard. Chris yells

Turn to page 4.

4

and you see that he has also been hauled out.

Your captors are wearing long, flowing robes and headdresses. Arabs, you suppose. What are Arabs doing at the professor's house?

Then you realize you aren't at the professor's at all. There is sand everywhere, and a few scraggly trees are growing over to your left. Something moves by one of the trees. A camel?

"Where are we?" you yell to Chris, but your friend looks too dazed to answer. You see an angry red mark on the side of his face where his captor has hit him.

Just then you hear bells and shouting. You turn around. A caravan is coming: a long line of camels, some with riders, some with enormous packs. You think about the Bible story of Joseph's brothers selling him as a slave to a passing caravan—and you have a very bad feeling about this situation.

Another man from the group steps up with a long whip in his hand. He uncoils it and shakes it threateningly at you.

If only you could make them understand that you can't understand them!

The man holding you turns you over to the man with the whip and goes to chatter with the caravan drivers. This may be your big chance.

Choices: You try escaping (turn to page 9).
You stand obediently by the man with the whip (turn to page 14).

"What'd you set AL for?" you ask.

"The last thing on the computer, A.D. 70."

"Where? And what happened then?"

"Oops! I forgot to check the cartograph. Oh, well, we'll soon find out."

The machine settles and you step out into a street in a large, ancient city. You are on the side of a hill so that you can see over the great stone wall around the city.

Beyond that wall is another wall made of earth. But there are no gates in this wall.

"Do you know what that is?" you exclaim to Chris. "It's a siege wall, a wall built by attackers to trap a city and its population away from food, from water, from help."

"You mean this city's under attack?" Chris asks. You nod grimly, and look out once more.

The top of the earthen wall is lined with crosses—five hundred or more, you guess. And on every cross is a dying or dead man. The agonized shrieks of the crucified echo in your ears, and you want to get away.

Suddenly you hear shouting and the crashing of wood on stone. Running to the other side of the hill, you see that attackers are storming the walls of the city with battering rams and portable bridges. As the bronze-helmeted soldiers in red tunics pour into the city, you think you recognize them: Roman legionnaires.

Thousands of soldiers storm the city. The civilians begin swarming up the hill past where you and Chris are standing. They shout and gesture at you, but you cannot understand them.

You turn and look at the top of the hill. It is crowned by a beautiful white building. Marble columns decorated with gold line the front, and a large, walled courtyard surrounds it. You think it must be a palace—or a temple.

The soldiers charge up the hill. You and Chris stand rooted to the spot watching the people flee, trampling one another in their frenzy to get away from the flailing clubs, swords, and horses' hooves. As the soldiers cut their way through the crowd, stones begin raining down on them from rooftops.

Choices: **You follow the crowd to the temple (turn to page 8).**
You look for a quieter part of the city (turn to page 25).

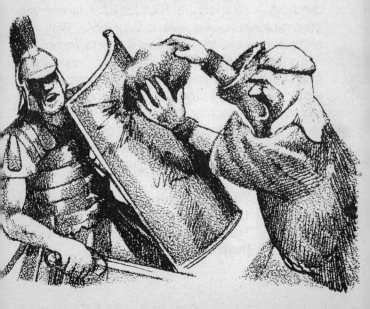

In spite of the rocks raining down on them like a giant hailstorm, the Roman troops charge up the hill.

Dodging stones and sword slashes yourself, you run ahead of them. When you reach the outer walls of the temple courtyard, you and Chris are both choking for breath—your throat dry and burning, your heart pounding so it shakes your whole body.

The defenders are blocking the soldiers' way to the building with their bodies. But one Roman soldier succeeds in throwing a burning torch through a window into one of the temple chambers.

The defenders rush to put out the flames. Even some of the soldiers help. Other citizens are trying to rescue objects from inside: golden candlesticks, lamps, scrolls. They look familiar to you from pictures you've seen in your Bible. Why, this isn't just any old temple. This is God's Temple in Jerusalem! And it's on fire. Even from outside you can see the flames leap up the cedar paneled walls, and smoke pours out the windows.

You look across the courtyard and see another torch thrown against a Temple gate. In all the confusion, no one seems to notice this new menace to the sacred building.

Choices: **You try to put it out (turn to page 12).**
You leave this dangerous scene (turn to page 17).

You start to run. That deadly whip cracks out at you like a cobra striking. You fall to the ground and roll toward the man, grabbing handfuls of sand as you roll.

As you come up, you aim both handfuls of sand at your assailant's eyes.

Your aim is good! He drops the whip to rub his eyes. You grab at the whip and lash at him.

Chris is struggling with his captor, but not making much headway. You lash in that direction. The enemy yells something, but he holds onto Chris.

Your assailant is coming back now.

Crack! You lash at him, and he backs off.

Chris's captor pulls a knife out of his belt. The sun glances menacingly off its sharp blade.

You lash at his knife hand with the whip, and it coils around his wrist. But instead of you jerking the knife out of his hand, he pulls the whip from yours.

In the confusion, Chris wrenches free. You sprint for the machine, Chris just a step behind you.

Suddenly Chris screams. You turn and see that the flying knife has struck his arm. He falters, but you grab him, pull him into the machine, slam the door, and lock it.

Chris is slumped at your feet, his arm bleeding beneath the gleaming silver handle of the knife.

If only you knew how to run this contraption. You push a button and close your eyes.

Turn to page 10.

10

After a few trembling shivers and beeping sounds, the machine quiets. Chris groans.

Your friend needs help. You take a deep breath, grasp the door handle, and look out cautiously. The door is wrenched angrily from your hands and you look up into a pair of scowling black eyes. The professor's eyes.

"I — we . . . I'm sorry," you stammer.

The professor doesn't answer. He is bending into the machine, holding Chris. "There's a first aid kit in the cupboard." He indicates the direction with a jerk of his head. "Get it."

You run across the room, find the blue and white kit, and rush back to the professor with it. He now has Chris lying on the floor and is examining the knife wound, having set the knife aside.

You gasp. The knife's silver handle is now tarnished with a thick black crust. It looks old. Hundreds of years old. Thousands, maybe.

Professor Quinten does an efficient, expert job of applying salves and bandages to your friend's arm and face. Chris sits up. He is woozy.

"He's all right. But he's lost rather a lot of blood. Needs something to eat and a big glass of juice." The professor, one arm supporting Chris, leads the way to the kitchen. He still looks angry.

Something weird is going on here.

Choices: You follow them to the kitchen (turn to page 13).
You bolt for the door (turn to page 148).

By some miracle you arrive back in the laboratory, but not before the professor has returned to discover your misdeed. You and Chris emerge from the machine, heads down and eyes on the floor. You feel the professor's glare burning a hole in the top of your head.

"I hope you learned your lesson," he snaps. "Now go."

He strides to the door and holds it open until you and Chris slink through. You don't look up until you hear the door slam behind you.

THE END

You rush toward the flaming torch. "Come on, help me! you shout at Chris over your shoulder.

You run through the fighting in the outer courtyard, tripping over fallen bodies, both Roman and Jewish, as you go.

In spite of your desperate effort, by the time you reach the gate of the sanctuary it is hopeless. The flames have spread too quickly.

Chris yells from behind you. "Look out! The wall is crumbl . . ."

The next thing you know, you're back at the professor's, and he's applying a cold cloth to a lump on your forehead.

"What happened?" you ask weakly.

"You were out cold, so I dragged you down the hill to the machine," Chris replies.

"What about the battle? And the Temple?"

"It was destroyed in A.D. 70," the professor says. "There's one thing you should realize about time travel. You can visit history. But you can't change it."

THE END

In the kitchen, the professor pours a big glass of orange juice for each of you. "Now, suppose you tell me what happened."

"Well . . ." You and Chris take turns telling of your adventure. The professor listens, not showing any emotion on his face.

When you finish, he folds his arms across his chest and leans back in his chair. "So it worked! I was sure it would."

He sounds pleased—not at all mad. You and Chris stare at him with your mouths open. No lecture? No calls to your parents? No police?

"I'll admit I was pretty angry at you two at first," he says. "But I'm also excited about my invention. Come on. I'll explain it to you."

Turn to page 18.

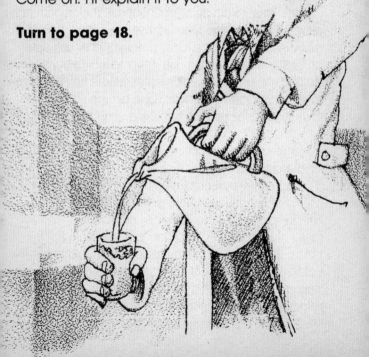

The new adversary shakes the whip at you threateningly and points toward the caravan. You take it that he means for you to walk in that direction. You go.

Chris is being dragged along. Your friend is definitely getting the worst of this deal.

The air is full of angry yelling, the tinkle of camel bells, and the stench of sweating camels. When you look toward the sun you can see waves of heat rising.

The man who had held you is arguing loudly with the man at the head of the caravan. You wish you could understand what they are yelling about because you're pretty sure it has to do with you.

You are dragged in front of the caravan leader. He pokes you in the ribs, pinches the muscle of your arms, and pulls your mouth open to look at your teeth. His own teeth are yellow snags with gaping black holes where several are missing. When he bends to examine your teeth, you almost pass out from the smell of his bad breath.

He shoves you away, shakes his head emphatically.

You've been rejected!

The slave trader moves on down the line. He hardly gives Chris a glance, but then after such rough treatment, Chris can barely stand up.

The trader stops in front of a strong, handsome youth being pushed forward by several others. You notice that one of the others is carrying a brightly colored coat over his arm.

The trader grasps a handful of the boy's dark, curly hair and tips his head back roughly, examining his eyes, ears, mouth. Then he grunts approval. A bag of coins is tossed to one of the sellers, and the trader moves off, pulling his new possession behind him.

You blink at what you've just seen. Your imagination is going wild. You were just thinking about Joseph being sold into slavery by his brothers, and . . . Maybe this is the set of an Arabian movie. It has to be.

The caravan starts slowly off across the desert. Chris is tossed in a heap on the sand beside you. Your captors walk off, shaking their heads, gesturing wildly and still arguing.

"Chris, come on, let's go!" You pull on your friend's arm, half leading, half dragging him back to the machine. You shove him into his seat. "Now, to get us home—I hope." You press a button.

Turn to page 11.

"Come on!" Chris says again.

"Just a minute!" You want to know what the machine is. You don't want your friend to think you're a chicken, but. . .

The decision is made for you as the professor strides back into the room.

"Now, then, what was I saying?" He gazes around the room as if looking for something he's misplaced. His eyes rest on the silver egg. "Ah, yes."

As he walks over to it, Chris comes around the corner, looking rather sheepish. You're glad you weren't inside it when the professor came back.

Turn to page 18.

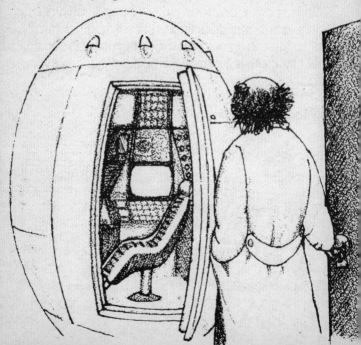

"It's hopeless," you say, shaking your head.

You both turn away from the burning battle and race down the hill to the time machine.

"I think I want to go back to the professor's," Chris says. Soon you're back, as if nothing had happened. . . .

Turn to page 27.

"Now then, watch," Professor Q orders. He reaches out a long, bony finger and touches a button on the smooth surface of the apparatus.

You start to ask what part you should watch, when the whole thing seems to disappear before your eyes. You gasp, blink, and look around the room. So does Chris.

The professor sees your reaction and laughs—a deep-toned, jerky laugh that seems to come all the way from his toes. This guy is weirder than his machine.

"It's still there," he says. "Look again."

You blink, and, sure enough: it is there. Chris asks the questions you're thinking. "What is it? How did it do that?"

"This, my young visitors, is something mankind has dreamed of for centuries. I have perfected a true time machine. I've long had the voltaic, magnetic, and galvanic computations necessary. But only recently, by borrowing technology from the United States Air Force, have I been able to achieve invisibility."

"Borrowed? From the Air Force?" Chris probes.

The professor laughs again. "No state secrets, I assure you. It was all in the public library! Now, as I was saying, the invisibility happens because, instead of directly reflecting the light, the paint absorbs the rays, and electronically it can send out signals which your brain interprets as being elsewhere."

"So that button turns on the electronic signal." You understand that much. "Why is invisibility important for a time machine?"

"Well, really, how would it look to show up in the middle of some ancient temple in a thing like that? Might be very complicated indeed."

You and Chris look at each other. Your brain is buzzing, trying to make sense out of what you are seeing—or rather, not seeing.

"How does the time part work?"

"Well," the professor begins, "the problem with most people's concept of time is that they think time is linear. That is, they think that once some-thing's happened—once time has passed—then it's gone forever. But that's not true."

"It's not?" you say.

"No, it's not. I have discovered a dimension that is beyond time. In this dimension, you can travel from time period to time period just as you, in normal life, travel from city to city. All of time is there, so to speak."

"Wait a minute." You are struggling to under-stand all this, and remembering some science fiction books you've read. "You mean those crazy theories that all time exists simultaneously are true?"

The professor smiles and gives a little nod. "That's right. It's just a matter of where you're looking from."

Turn to page 20.

"So, where we live is just someone's picture?" Chris asks.

"Yes," the professor agrees. "Someone with a capital S."

You are about to ask what that means when

you hear Chris's voice.

"Can we try it out?"

You wish he hadn't said that.

Turn to page 22.

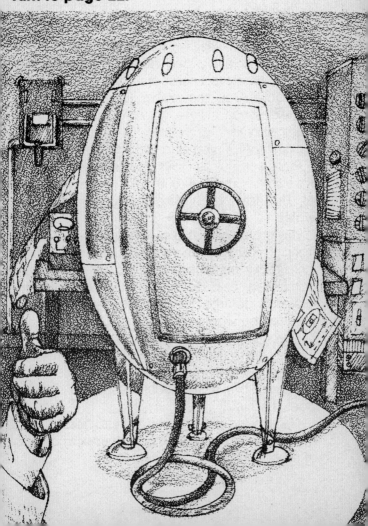

The professor gropes a bit and finds the button to turn off the electronic signal. The machine reappears. He opens the door to reveal two cushioned chairs with seat belts, a panel of instrument gauges, a keyboard much like a typewriter's, and three tv screens.

"Come on in and sit down so you can see better," he invites.

He points to two long, narrow rectangles. One shows lighted red numbers. "Two chronometers, or clocks. One shows ship time. The other will show destination time, when AL knows what your destination is."

"Who's AL?" you and Chris say together.

Professor Quinten lays his hand gently on the typewriter. "This is AL5001, but you can call him AL. He'll take you where you want to go. Now, watch."

The professor flips a switch and the screens in front of you light up. "Wow! Three CRTs," says Chris. Your friend has been a bit nutty about computers for quite a while now. If he and the professor get into computer talk, you'll be stuck here for the whole day.

"Wrong, my friend. These are not cathode-ray tubes, these are plasma display screens — nothing but the newest and best for AL."

"Yeah? I've read about those. How much K does it have?"

"Two hundred fifty-six megabytes." Chris's mouth falls open at such an astounding amount of memory in the machine.

The professor continues. "AL's magnetic bubble memory system is extensive, but not infinite. Actually he's rather limited." He points to the screen on the left. "This is the chronograph." The screen in the center prints, **"MODE?"**

The professor types "CHR RUN," and the chronograph screen begins printing out a list of dates and historical events. They flash by quickly and you wonder how long it's going to take them to get up to your birthday when the flashing figures suddenly stop at A.D. 70.

"I'm afraid that's it." The professor sounds almost apologetic. "Of course, my full-sized computer here is unlimited, but the on-board computer isn't.

"Now, the capsule flies in space as well as time." Again AL asks "MODE?" and the professor answers "CART RUN." On the screen to the right appears a map of Europe, the Middle East, and Northern Africa. The professor turns a dial and a small gray square moves over the map. "To locate a desired position, put the cartograph's gray square over the spot on the map, and push this button." As he says that the screen is filled with what had been just the tiny space inside the gray square. "You may recognize this as Egypt."

Turn to page 24.

24

"Now to select a city . . . " The gray dot moves again, the button is pushed, and a map of the city of Cairo is before you.

"Oh, boy!" You can tell Chris is just itching to get his hands on that equipment.

"Why is that all the map there is?" you ask. "Couldn't this thing fly to other places?"

"Of course, if it were programmed to do so. But I chose the time you saw on the chronograph and that area on the cartograph because biblical archaeology is a hobby of mine. Those are the areas **I'm** most anxious to visit. Now, one more thing . . ."

Ding dong. The doorbell startles all of you.

"What now?!" Professor Quinten stalks to the door, obviously irritated by so many interruptions in one morning.

"Well, come on. What are we waiting for?" Chris jumps into the machine and starts buckling a seat belt. "He said we could, didn't he? So let's go." Chris starts adjusting the dials.

"Don't you think we ought to wait until he comes back?"

"Why? He explained it all to me. It's really pretty simple. I've done lots of stuff on my dad's office computer, programmed games and things, you know. This is no different."

"Well . . ." You are anxious to try it out.

Choices: You go now (turn to page 6).
You wait for the professor (turn to page 27).

It's not hard to find a quieter area. As the crowd of people and soldiers surge up the hill, the center of the city is left empty.

You walk down a street of small houses that at first look deserted. But as you come nearer you hear wailing through many of the open windows and doorways. On one doorstep a small child sits crying to herself. It's easy to see why. Her tiny arms and legs are nothing but bones with the skin stretched tight over them; her stomach is distended like a balloon. You've seen pictures of famine on tv. You know she's starving.

In the next yard you see a small body crumpled in a heap. This one is not crying anymore. You think of the half-eaten bowl of cornflakes you threw out this morning.

As you near the outer walls, the action heats up. "Watch out!" you jump and yell as a huge boulder comes hurtling over the wall.

You are intrigued by the bits of Roman war machines you see sticking up over the wall. "Let's get a better look at this," you say to Chris.

You climb the outer stairway to the roof of a nearby building. From there you can see Roman catapults hurling great stones like the one that almost got you, battering rams, mobile towers with bridges, and iron-pointed machines that seem to bore right through walls.

The Jewish troops have clubs, spears, and arrows—none of them very effective, since the

Turn to page 26.
Turn to page 26.

Romans also have iron-plated shield walls that move ahead of their attacking force.

For a while you are fascinated. This is like watching an historical war movie on a wrap-around screen. Then you walk over to the other side of the roof and look down into a courtyard. A mother is sobbing over a dead child in her arms.

You and Chris, feeling sobered, walk slowly back down the stairs and turn up the hill, still following the wall, but away from the battle.

A line of people is moving slowly toward the wall from a side street. Several carry the bodies of children in their arms. Others pull body-laden stretchers or carts. Obviously this is a funeral procession. The sad little group walks to the wall where they hand the bodies they are carrying to men on ladders. The dead are thrown over the wall to lie in unburied piles on the desert sand.

You stand in silent respect of their mourning. As they return from their sorrowful task, a woman looks up at you from the dusty ground. Her hollow, sunken eyes blink and then focus.

She begins shouting hysterically and pointing at the two of you. Roused from their mourning and nearly dead from hunger themselves, the crowd is easily frenzied by the sight of your strange clothing.

Choices: You run (turn to page 31).
You try to calm them (turn to page 36).

"Now, as I was saying . . ." Professor Quinten comes back into his laboratory to join you. "What **was** I saying?"

"I think you were going to show us some more about the controls, sir," you suggest politely.

"Ah, yes." He points to a red button just to the right of the keyboard. "This is the emergency travel abort. It interrupts all systems and brings you straight back here."

That could be handy, you are thinking.

The professor steps out of the machine. "And there's something else," he adds. He pulls two robes out of a box. "Here. One of you go in the kitchen and one in the bathroom and change into these."

Soon you emerge in costume. You see that Chris is scowling at his skirtlike hem and bare legs. "I look like a girl," he says.

Turn to page 28.

The professor smiles. "No, you're dressed as a boy. And it's important that you both be identified as boys," he says, handing you braided headbands which you put on at forehead level. "'Girls were rather restricted in the things they could do then. And of course, they married very young. Wouldn't want you to wind up as somebody's wife." Chris looks horror-stricken.

Your robe is a loose-fitting garment of a coarsely woven brown fabric. Your tennis shoes are replaced by a pair of rope-soled sandals.

"Most of the children you encounter will be barefoot, but since your feet aren't hardened to the hot sand and rough roads, these will be expedient," the professor explains.

You finally start to take your seats in the extraordinary cylinder. "Wait," orders the professor.

He hands you each a small box that looks something like a pocket calculator. "Translators," he says. "All the major languages of that time and area — Greek, Hebrew, Latin, Aramaic, Egyptian — are programmed into AL, and this links you to AL by radio waves. You'll hear other people's speech translated through this tiny device." He puts something like a miniature hearing aid in Chris's ear. "And your words will be translated and transmitted through a speaker in this." He hangs the translator box around your neck and tucks it behind your robe.

"This is better than at the United Nations. They have to wear big headphones there," you say.

"Now can we go?" asks Chris. The professor nods. You jump into your seats and buckle up.

The door of the machine closes. You and Chris grin at each other excitedly.

The door opens and the professor sticks his head in again. "I almost forgot to tell you. You'll be a part of the time you choose, so be careful. You won't be just watching it on tv. You could get hurt. So think before you make your choices!"

He closes the door and you and Chris are alone with AL.

"Well, where shall we go?" you ask as Chris switches on the chronograph. "How about Rome? Caesar and chariot races and all that." "That'd be OK. Or how about Egypt? You know, King Tut, and building the pyramids?"

Choices: **You tell Chris to type in Rome during the time of the Caesars (turn to page 33).**
You tell him to take you to Egypt (turn to page 32).

No use trying to reason with a mob, especially a mob yelling at you in a foreign language. You and Chris run down a narrow street, turn into an alley, and scramble behind some bushes.

Just when you think you've lost them, you hear new shouting. You know the bushes you've taken cover in are too scraggly to hide you for long, so you start running again.

Oh, no; bad choice. The passageway you've turned into is a dead end. You hear feet pounding the pavement behind you.

Chris dives through the open window of a home. The angry mob is within a stone's throw of you now, and that's just what they do—start throwing stones at you.

"Here!" yells Chris. You dive in the window after him, getting up just in time to see him run through a doorway on the other side of the room. Meanwhile, the yelling horde is stuck outside the narrow window, blocking each other's way.

You run down another street, duck into a dark alley, and flatten yourselves against the wall. Finally the harsh shouts in the distance become quiet.

"Let's go find AL," Chris says. "I want to go home!"

So you do. . . .

Turn to page 27.

"Take us to ancient Egypt," Chris types in.

"TIME?" AL asks.

Chris looks at you. "What year?"

You shrug. "I don't know much about Egypt." Then you remember Professor Q's mention of Bible archaeology. The Bible talked about Egypt, didn't it?

"I learned about Egypt in Sunday school," you say. Chris perks up a bit. "You know, how the Hebrews were slaves, and how God had Moses put plagues on Egypt till Pharaoh let them go."

"What are plagues?"

"Oh, disasters, I guess," you reply. "Frogs popping up all over. Water turning into blood."

"Really?" Sometimes Chris has a real taste for the gruesome.

"Yeah. So Pharaoh let the Hebrews go, and they went to the Promised Land and fought a bunch of battles and conquered it."

"I'd like to see those battles," Chris murmurs.

You and Chris discuss your options and then Chris tells AL what you'd like to see.

"Archaeology is not an exact science," AL prints out, "so the precise dates of the events you mention are not known. But I will do my best."

Choices: You told AL to try to get you to Egypt while the Hebrews were slaves (turn to page 37).
You decided to see the Israelites battle their way into the Promised Land (go to page 40).

With visions of chariots charging down wide boulevards, you tell AL to take you to Rome.

The lights blink and the dials whir, and then suddenly you are deafened by a terrible crashing noise. It's a good thing you and Chris fastened your seat belts because you are tossed forward and backward. Then it feels like you are being thrown up into the air, only to have the bottom drop out from under you and come crashing back down.

"What's wrong?" you yell, gripping the sides of your seat.

Chris looks ghostly white. "The machine must be malfunctioning! It never did this before."

"Shall I open the door?"

"We don't have anything to lose," Chris gasps. "We'll get beaten to death in here."

You open the door, and a great slosh of salt water hits you in the face. You hear voices.

Turn to page 34.

"Let it run with the wind!"

"Strike the sails!"

"Secure the lifeboat!"

Your time machine didn't malfunction. It brought you down onto a huge sailing ship—in the middle of a storm at sea.

"I thought you set AL for Rome."

Chris frowns. "Slight miscalculation, I guess."

"Here, you!" A sailor points at you. "Hold this fast while I lash it down." You hold the rope with one hand and the deck rail with the other, hoping that you won't get seasick.

There are dozens of sailors rushing everywhere, tying things down, securing latches, and struggling with the sails. The man who appears to be the captain strides down the deck, shouting orders. He points to you and Chris. "Give a hand below deck. We've got to haul the cargo out."

He strides off, and you and Chris stumble toward the stairs. At least you won't have to worry about getting washed overboard if you go inside. You hope the time capsule is secure.

You're right about not getting washed off deck down below—but that's its only advantage. The tossing seems much more violent from below decks. You are thrown from side to side. The air is so hot and close, you feel like you'll suffocate.

"I'm going to be sick." Chris, hand over mouth, rushes back up the stairs.

You have an uneasy feeling that you may be joining your friend any minute, but you keep on going. The hold is full of sacks of grain, which the seamen are lugging up to throw overboard. There seem to be tons of it. The stuff must be awfully valuable, and it's a shame to waste it. But an expensive cargo won't do the men any good if they drown. And if they drown, you drown. You start tugging at the heavy sacks, too.

It seems like you've worked for hours when a strong-featured passenger with reddish hair and a beard comes down to stand in the midst of the hold. He announces, "Men, you should have listened to me and not left Crete. We could have avoided this storm. But now I tell you to be of good cheer. There will be no lost lives among us, though the ship will be lost."

Who is this guy? And how does he know? you wonder to yourself.

"Last night an angel of the God I serve stood beside me and said, 'Fear not, Paul. You must stand trial before Caesar, and God will protect all those that sail with you.' So keep up your courage, men!"

You see Chris tugging rather weakly at a sack of wheat.

"Hey, now I know what's happening," you say. "That's Paul! You know, he wrote a lot of those letters in the Bible, and he's going to Rome. Shall we go with him?"

Choices: You follow Paul (turn to page 39).
You get back to the time machine (turn to page 69).

You walk toward the screaming woman. You are shaking, but you hold your hands out, palms up, and try to smile at her.

"Please," you plead, "We aren't doing anything wrong. We won't hurt anybody. There's nothing to be afraid of."

At the sound of your foreign language, others begin screaming, too.

You are seized by many hands and dragged toward the wall. What are they going to do with you? Throw you over with the dead bodies? Give you to their soldiers? Or to the Romans? If only you could make them understand. . . .

THE END

The machine whirs and jerks. It all makes you a little nervous, so you're glad when the indicator lights quit blinking and you can open the door.

"Yuck!" you yell. Every step you take makes a squishing sound, and the ground feels slimy under your feet. Chris grabs onto the door of the machine to keep from slipping and falling down.

You think for a minute. AL must have hit the plagues on Egypt right on the button. Now, what were they? Water turning to blood . . . frogs . . .

"Lice!" you announce when you remember. "The dust of the earth turned into lice." Gross. You think you're going to be sick to your stomach. "Let's try something else."

Chris agrees, and you push the next button.

"You didn't change AL's time setting! Doesn't feel like it did much," Chris says as you open the door.

He may be right. You no sooner step out than you are attacked by a cloud of flies. Big, fat, black, buzzing flies, swarming everywhere. Waving your arms wildly to beat them off, you jump back into the machine. Unfortunately, a lot of flies get in the machine with you.

Choices: You'd rather be anywhere but Egypt, so you hit a button randomly (turn to page 144).
You want to give Egypt another try, so you hit the same button again (turn to page 42).

"Twenty fathoms."

"Fifteen fathoms."

"We must be nearing land!"

Seamen and passengers are rushing madly about. Approaching land sounds good—but you hear someone muttering about rocks.

"I urge you to eat before we attempt going ashore," Paul directs. Even though he's a prisoner, he seems to hold as much authority over the crew as the captain. When the hasty meal of dried meat and hard bread is over, dawn comes. The ship's crew scouts the coastline for a suitable place to land.

"A beach, just past the boulders there. See?"

"Make for it, men," the captain orders.

The crew takes up the anchors, loosens the rudders, hoists the foresail to the wind.

Suddenly the smooth gliding of the ship is brought to an abrupt, jolting stop. The hull grates sickeningly on a sandbar just below the surface of the water.

"Everyone overboard!" the captain shouts.

A soldier yells, "Kill the prisoners! We cannot let any of them swim out and escape!"

But the centurion overrules him. "No! Kill no one. Anyone who can swim should jump into the sea and make for land. The rest of us can hang on to planks and float ashore."

The ship shudders and gives a rending creak, then an ominous groan. . . .

Turn to page 41.

You have landed outside the walls of a great city, and it looks as if someone is having a parade. People line the top of the wall, packed as solidly together as the stones of the wall itself.

Marching around the wall is a whole army of men carrying spears. In the center of the military procession are seven old men in long blue robes with jeweled vests and fancy headdresses. They are carrying trumpets made of animal horns. Behind them, four more men in robes walk, each holding the end of a long pole. The poles support a box.

You notice that the box—or whatever it is—is covered with a blue cloth so you can't see it. You do know one thing. From the way everyone in the procession is acting, the box is very important.

You watch for a few minutes, then realize this isn't exactly a normal parade. At least it's not a very friendly one. The people on the wall shout at the marchers angrily and throw things at them.

Choices: You follow the marchers around the wall (turn to page 44).
You sneak into the city and join the watchers on the wall (turn to page 76).

"Now!" the centurion shouts. "Jump!"

You and Chris leap overboard with the others and swim for shore. You are good swimmers and make it easily. Behind you, you see others floating in, clinging to planks and barrels.

Then you hear a thunderous crashing and tearing noise. You look out to sea in time to see the great mainsail of the ship toppled into the water like a giant tree sawed down. The bow of the ship remains stuck to the shoal, but the stern is torn apart by the violence of the waves.

You have a grim thought. The time machine was in the stern. "Oh, no! We're stuck here forever!"

Chris stands looking at the wreck, not answering you for several minutes. You begin to think your friend's in shock. "Chris! Speak to me!"

"I'm thinking."

"Yeah, I noticed."

"I'm not so sure we're stuck. AL's door seals very tightly. The machine is metal, and I bet it's watertight. Maybe we could swim out to it or something."

"Swim out to what? It's invisible, remember?" You also think going back into the water could be risky.

Choices: You stay on the island with Paul (turn to page 46).
You attempt to swim to the time machine (turn to page 48).

"Now this is more like it!" Chris says as you step out onto a quiet street lined with mudbrick houses. The sun is setting, orange on the horizon.

"It must be suppertime," you say. "Smell that roast meat? Yum!"

"So what do we do? Knock on a door and invite ourselves in?"

"That would be rude, wouldn't it?" You kick the ground and hit your toe on something hard.

"Hey, look!" It's a small leather pouch, filled with something metal. You open it, reach in, and come out with a handful of copper rings, crude and unevenly shaped. You begin sorting them out, slipping bands of different sizes on your fingers. "Wonder what they're for?" you say.

"Well," Chris answers, "that bag they're in looks like a money pouch. I wonder if these could be some sort of primitive coin."

You spread your fingers, examining the copper pieces encircling each one. "Could be. If you're right, think how valuable they must be!"

"I don't know. After all, they're copper. At home, copper pieces are just pennies."

"I don't mean valuable here. I mean for coin collectors or museums or something."

Chris gets the picture. "Yeah, you're right. A whole bag. In pretty good condition, too."

Choices: You take the coins home with you
(turn to page 45).
You look for their owner (turn to
page 47).

You fall into step behind the rear guard. This is a big city to be marching around. You begin to think it is an awfully silly way for an army to be spending time. No wonder the people on the wall are making fun of the group.

After a while, you decide to get a closer look at that box the robed men are carrying. You work your way ahead of the guard, and are soon right behind the men carrying the poles that support it.

You're just wondering if the box is heavy when one of the men stumbles and loses his grip on the pole. The box is falling toward you!

Choices: You try to help (turn to page 50).
You let it go (turn to page 61).

You stuff the bag in the front of your robe and head back to the machine, trying not to think about who might have dropped it.

It isn't really stealing, you argue with yourself. **After all, it's really thousands of years from now and all these people are really dead anyway.** Well, aren't they? It's all rather confusing.

You wonder how you'll explain having the rings when you get ready to sell them. Probably have to tell a pack of lies.

After you get into the machine and buckle your seat belt, Chris shuts the door, and you take off. Soon you feel the capsule settle itself back at the professor's, and you reach for the bag of copper rings you set beside you.

It's gone! You look on the floor, behind the seat—everywhere inside the capsule. All you find is dust and sand.

Chris shrugs. "Well, so much for getting rich quick."

You nod your head sadly. "I guess those rings must have belonged to that time, and they were supposed to stay there—or else come to the twentieth century the same way they would have anyway," you say slowly, running your finger through a little pile of copper colored dust by the seat.

THE END

You stay on shore rather than venture out into the choppy waters again. There is great rejoicing when every person from the ship gets safely to land. Now lots of debris from the broken vessel is washing in. You and Chris help the sailors rescue everything they can. Every time a crate of food or bundle of clothing is pulled from the water, the men cheer. Every provision you can salvage will make your survival that much more likely.

After hours of working knee-deep in the foaming, salty water, your legs are numb with cold. Your feet are cut and bruised from the rocks along the beach. But you have a good supply of stores. Finally you and Chris sit down to rest.

"Looks like we're stuck here," Chris says.

"Yeah, but it might not be too bad. Paul's a pretty interesting guy."

"I'd rather live in the twentieth century," says Chris. "You know, the professor said he planned to build other machines. Maybe he can pick up some kind of a signal from AL — even if he is a little wet — and come and get us."

"Yeah, I bet he can! In the meantime, we'll probably get to Rome. Paul is supposed to stand trial before Caesar," you recall.

"Um, how would we get to Rome from here?" Chris asks suspiciously.

"By ship, of course."

Chris groans and puts his hand on his stomach. "I was afraid you'd say that. . . ."

THE END

"Maybe someone dropped them. Guess we could knock on a few doors and ask if anyone lost anything," Chris suggests.

The first house on the road is the largest. "They might carry around a bag of money," you say.

Apparently not, or else they are too rich to have missed it, because the gate of the courtyard is slammed in your face.

Chris shrugs. "Let's go back the other way, down near the river. I saw some sort of shacky places there—bet they'd be glad to be offered a bag of money or whatever that stuff is."

You walk for some time in the direction Chris indicated. As you go you notice the houses getting smaller and poorer. Then you come to an area where there are no houses at all.

Following Chris's lead, you approach another group of huts. You hear the gentle lapping of a river against its banks. These houses appear to be made of small sticks or reeds, giving the impression of being enormous baskets.

You start to knock on the first door when you notice strange red marks on each side of the door and over the top. Something drips on your forehead. You wipe it off. It's blood!

"Gross! There's blood all around this door!"

Chris looks up and down the road. "Yeah, lots of the houses have it. I don't like the looks of this."

Choices: You leave (turn to page 45).
You knock (turn to page 54).

You stand at the water's edge for a long time, looking at the tossing waves and the debris from the ship.

"See anything?" asks Chris.

"Not really. But there seems to be a pretty large concentration of broken wood and stuff just beyond those boulders there."

"Think we should wait and see if it gets washed ashore?" Chris suggests. "We could just walk up and down the beach and hope to stumble over it."

You shake your head. "I think the chances of it getting smashed on those rocks out there are greater than the chances of it being washed to shore in one piece."

"OK, let's swim," Chris says. "If we get tired, there's always all that wood floating around to grab onto."

You plunge into the icy water. The first wave swamps you, and you fight your way back up, spitting and choking. When the same thing happens on the next wave you decide you need a new plan. When the third breaker rolls toward you, you're ready for it. You dive right through it and come up on the far side. Now, that's better.

When you're out about even with the boulders, you begin encountering pieces of wreckage. You decide to tread water for a bit and look for any unusual patterns that could indicate a large invisible object floating by.

It seems like hours that you maneuver in that icy water checking out pieces of soaked cargo and bits of splintered wood. Then it happens.

A cramp. It starts at your ankle and shoots all the way up your left calf. You cry out with pain and grab your leg. As you do, you sink and gulp down a lot of seawater. You fight your way to the surface, thrashing, flailing, and yelling. You think you hear Chris answer from a long way off, but you know he'll never make it to you in time.

Choices: **You keep yelling and trying to swim (turn to page 55).**
You try to relax and float on your back (turn to page 63).

You rush forward without thinking, shoving the guards around you aside. The box is sliding downward. Everyone seems frozen with horror. Just before it hits the ground, the fallen man grasps the end of the pole and tries to lift it again. But it's heavy.

You rush to his side and support his arm with both of yours. Together you push upward and bring the mysterious box to a level position once more.

Then you realize a crowd has gathered. The people around you are cheering.

"He has saved the holy ark!"

"He has protected the stone tablets on which Jehovah gave the Ten Commandments to Moses."

"Let us take him to Joshua, our leader!" You are lifted on the shoulders of the crowd.

Turn to page 56.

You are outside the walls of a great city. The walls of heavy, hewn stones rise several stories high and are as thick as a modern street is wide. There are guard towers spaced along the top of the wall and Roman soldiers pacing back and forth. A big dark tunnel gapes in the middle of the wall, like a lion with its mouth open wide. The gates of the city are open.

"Well, I told AL to bring us to Jerusalem, so I guess this is it," you say.

"Looks like we're not the only ones who chose Jerusalem today," comments Chris. The road leading to the city is choked with people. Most of them are dusty and a bit ragged, as if they've traveled a long way.

"Bet they wish they had an AL to travel in," you joke.

Suddenly you hear shouting and cheering behind you. The mass of people that choked the road are now pushing to the side of it to leave a path in the middle. Children and young men are climbing palm trees, pulling down the branches, and passing them out among the people.

"Looks like a parade!" Chris says in your ear.

You shrug and hand your friend a palm branch. "Let's get a better view," you say, and begin edging to the side of the road.

The shouts urge you along. You don't want to miss the sight.

"Hosanna!" "There, I see him!"

Turn to page 52.

"Blessed is the king who comes in the name of the Lord!" "The king! The king!"

When you and Chris finally catch a glimpse of what all the fuss is about, you see only a rather simply dressed man, riding on a donkey.

"What's the big deal?" Chris asks. "He doesn't look like a king."

Someone near you turns to explain. "It is Jesus, the prophet from Nazareth."

Jesus? You'd suspected that it might be. Now you strain to see his face. It seems that he will pass by you without even turning in your direction, however—until a couple of richly attired older men call out to him.

"Why do you let your followers make such a disturbance right under the nose of the Romans?" one asks disapprovingly. "You should silence them!"

Jesus turns, and you see a very ordinary Jewish face. But you can sense strength in his eyes and voice. "If the people are quiet," he replies to his questioners, "the very stones will cry out!"

Then his donkey plods on. The crowd closes in behind him and follows him through the gate into the city, where more cheering throngs wait.

"Want to see where he's going?" you ask Chris.

"Actually, I'd like to find something to eat first," Chris answers.

Choices: You follow Jesus (turn to page 59).
You go to look for food (turn to page 78).

54

"Something about this is familiar." You wish you felt as smart as you sound. "Let's ask about the blood this time and see what happens."

But you don't get to ask, because when you get up to the door you hear people inside arguing. The translator in your ear speaks a split second after their actual voices.

"How could you have been so careless?"

"Mother, I don't know. How many times do I have to say I'm sorry?"

"Saying 'I'm sorry' doesn't buy the salt and bitter herbs Moses instructed us to eat tonight. Do you think that this is just any night? Do you think we can eat like the Egyptians tonight?"

The door is open. You stand there, holding the bag in your hand. Finally the boy who had apparently lost the money notices you.

"Mother, there it is! It is returned!"

The woman sees you and what you're holding. She rushes to grab the bag. "Praise be to God! We are saved!" She turns to her son. "Quickly, run to the market and purchase what we need. And hold the bag more tightly this time!"

The boy runs off, clutching the pouch in both hands. You start to leave, too, but the mother and several children gather around you. "Wait, don't go!" "You must eat the feast with us." "Without you we wouldn't have had one."

Choices: You stay (turn to page 58).

You decide to explore the city more (turn to page 62).

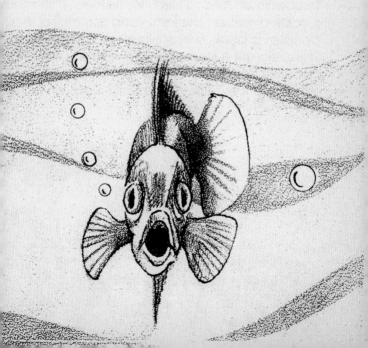

"Chris!" You cough and sputter, because you keep getting seawater in your mouth. "Help!"

Chris is heading toward you, but he seems so far away.

Your leg is killing you. You know that when you get a cramp in bed at night, it helps to stand on it and walk around. You wonder how deep the sea is here. Perhaps you could stand on the bottom.

You take a deep breath and propel yourself downward. Suddenly you feel a strong current.

Oh, no! You forgot one important factor in ocean swimming: undertow. It's too strong for you in your breathless condition. Looks like this is **THE END.**

"Here is our hero, Joshua," explains one member of the throng as you are deposited on the ground again. You are now at the front of the procession, and a bronzed, authoritative man greets you. Joshua.

"Thank you for saving the honor of God's ark before the people of Jericho," Joshua says. "I don't think that the Lord would have allowed his holy vessel to touch the ground. Even without your aid, he would have found a way to preserve it. But your heart is in the right place for wanting to help."

You barely heard the last part of Joshua's compliment. Did he really say that this city was named Jericho? It's just like the song: "Joshua fit the battle of Jericho, Jericho, Jericho . . . "

Joshua waves one arm, and the rest of the people go back to their places in the formation. The procession begins again, and you fall into step with Joshua. Chris runs up to join you.

"Excuse me," you ask Joshua, "but why are you marching around the city?"

"Because the Lord told me to," Joshua explains. "He said that he would deliver Jericho into our hands. We march once around the city on each of six days. We've done that. This is the seventh day, and we are to march around seven times. After that, we'll all blow our horns and shout—and God will cause the city to fall."

"Wow," Chris says. "Think it'll work?"

You know the answer. You remember the rest of the song now. "Joshua fit the battle of Jericho, and the walls came a-tumblin' down." You look at the people on the wall. They're still jeering. Obviously they aren't taking the Israelites seriously—and they should.

Choices: You decide to stay with Joshua (turn to page 68).
You run into Jericho to warn the people of what will happen (turn to page 106).

You're glad you decided to stay. The roast lamb is delicious, although you're not too taken with the bitter herbs. You eat some, though, because your hosts seem to think it's pretty important. The bread is funny and flat, a lot like a soda cracker without any salt on it.

You expect the family to get ready for bed after they finish eating, but instead they begin packing their belongings, putting on robes, and tying sandals on the children's feet.

"Looks like you're getting ready to go on a trip, so I think we'll run along now," you say.

Your hosts are horrified. "No! You must not leave this house."

You must look puzzled, because one of the children asks, "Didn't you hear Moses' announcement?"

"Uh, no we didn't," you and Chris answer.

The father explains. "It is the Lord's Passover. Moses says that the Lord will pass through the land tonight to strike the firstborn sons of the Egyptians. But when he sees lamb's blood upon any doorpost, the Lord will pass over that door, and will not allow death to come into that house."

Sounds to you like a good reason to stay inside! There's time enough to go back to the capsule in the morning, you think sleepily.

Turn to page 97.

All along the wide boulevard, people are waving palm branches and shouting "Hosanna!" "The king of the Jews!" People are holding small children on their shoulders for a better view, and many hold out their hands to touch Jesus as he rides by.

You follow Jesus and the cheering crowds up a steep hill that overlooks the city. On the top of the hill is a beautiful building, its white stones gleaming in the sun. A wall encloses the building and its courtyard. Outside the wall, another crowd has gathered to wait for Jesus.

This crowd seems happy to see him, but they aren't jumping and cheering as the others have. They can't. Many are lame and crippled, sitting helplessly on little straw mats; sick children lie listlessly in their mother's arms; a blind man gropes through the crowd. You find the closeness of the mob all around you almost stifling. A little way from the crowd is an old woman wrapped in rags. She turns her face away from the other people, crying, "Unclean, unclean," and they move quickly away from her.

When Jesus rides up, the sick move toward him, holding out their arms imploringly and pleading for help. "Master, heal my child." "Lord, make me well." "Touch my eyes." The size of the crowd had overwhelmed you. You wonder how Jesus feels when so many people are looking to him for help.

Turn to page 60.
Turn to page 60.

He slips from the back of the donkey and grasps the limp hand of a sick child whose mother is kneeling before him. "Rise up, my child. Walk!" Jesus says in a clear, commanding voice.

The child immediately jumps from his mother's arms. The crowd murmurs its amazement and pushes closer. The mother has taken Jesus' hand and is thanking him over and over again.

"Awesome," says Chris. Meanwhile, as the crowds push closer to Jesus you and Chris are jostled farther away from him.

"That was really something!" says Chris after finding a seat on a large, flat stone. "How does he do it?"

You sit by Chris on the grassy hillside and recount what you can remember of your Sunday school lessons that told about Jesus healing people. "He's God's Son," you explain. "He's in a human body, but he has all God's power. He can do anything." Chris doesn't say much, but you can tell he is thinking.

After a while you see the crowd begin to move down the hill. "Let's see what's happening," you say. As you move closer you hear one of the followers near Jesus say something about being expected for dinner in Bethany. "Shall we go with them?" you ask Chris.

**Choices: Go to Bethany (turn to page 86).
Stay in Jerusalem (turn to page 78).**

You stand to one side, not sure what to do, as the golden box slides down the pole toward the ground. The other people around you seem frozen in horror.

But the carrier, who by his robes seems to be some kind of priest, regains his footing and lifts the golden pole again.

He looks at the people as if to chide them for their fear. "The Lord would not allow his holy ark, the Ark of the Covenant, to strike the ground!" he says. "He is a God of power. He has power to protect this holy vessel, just as he has power to deliver this city of Jericho into our hands!"

The people murmur agreement, and the march goes on. You fall into step again, but this time with more excitement.

"This must be the time when Joshua led the Israelites into battle against Jericho!" you exclaim to Chris.

He gives you a blank look. "If there's a war, what's with all this marching?"

You grin. "It's a surprise. You'll find out!"

Turn to page 68.

62

You go back up to the street where you found the copper rings. Chariots are pulling up to a large house there, and people wearing elegant flowing robes and gold jewelry are going in.

"Looks like some party! Bet we could sneak in there and get something to eat," Chris suggests.

"Wonder what Egyptians have for food," you say.

Choices: **You sneak in (turn to page 75). You walk on up the street in search of the Pharaoh's palace (turn to page 65).**

You roll limply onto your back, just as you learned in swimming lessons. You're better off not struggling. The waves are moving toward shore. At best, they'll take you to dry ground. At worst, they'll wash you onto a boulder where you can cling till help comes.

A piece of the broken mast swirls by your head and you grasp at it like a drowning man. You cling to the spar, heaving and sobbing to get your breath. The cramp has relaxed, but now you're too exhausted to do anything but hold on.

The waves are washing you toward the boulders. You hear the water breaking over the rocks. Your wave is next. You prepare your body for the bruising contact with granite.

The impact takes away the little bit of wind you have left, but you find a small handhold and you clasp it with all your strength. Your cheek rests on the smooth, cool surface, your eyes are closed.

Suddenly you open your eyes. What's this? You are grasping thin air! At least that's what it looks like.

You give a shout of triumph! You're holding on to the machine! Your tiny handhold is its invisibility button.

Chris swims to you and the two of you clamber aboard. You may look like drowned rats, but you're sure thankful you aren't.

"To Rome?" asks Chris.

"Yes," you manage to gasp. "The dry way."

Turn to page 71.

You wander the streets in the dark, looking for the palace. By the time you find it, standing inside a courtyard on a landscaped knoll at the center of the city, you're tired. You and Chris curl up in a shadowed corner for a nap.

In the morning, you walk up several broad marble steps to a colonnade running the complete length of the building. The columns on either side of the main entrance march two stories high and in rows three deep. The wall beyond the pillars is entirely covered with gold leaf, glistening in the sun, painted with exotic birds and flowers.

"Wow!" Chris says. "As rich as King Tut, all right. Maybe we can eat breakfast out of gold bowls!"

The doorway into the palace itself is guarded. Two pairs of armed guards stand outside the door and two pairs stand just inside. The sunlight glistens on their bronzed skin—and highlights their brawny muscles.

"I don't think we'd better try to go further," you whisper. "Could be risky."

Just then there is a commotion inside the doorway. The guards snap to attention.

"Where is my page? Where is my personal servant? Has the whole palace gone mad? Guards, I ordered my chariot—where is it?"

A guard rushes off along the colonnade and you and Chris jump back into the shadows. Your movement catches someone's eye.

Turn to page 66.

"And what is this creature?" The voice refers to you. Chris inches deeper into the shadows, unnoticed.

You hesitate. A guard points a spear at you. The speaker strides forward and you see him. Pharaoh.

"To judge by the costume, he is a Hebrew slave left behind, sir," the guard answers for you.

"He was wise to stay," Pharaoh says. "Those slaves that put a curse on our sons and plundered our jewels and fled will not live to see tomorrow!"

The Pharaoh turns to you. "I would like you to carry my shield. Then, when I have destroyed the Hebrews, you will see that their God is not as powerful as I am!"

A servant shoves a jeweled shield at you. It is so heavy you falter under its weight and almost drop it. You're glad no one caught Chris. Maybe he can figure out a way to rescue you. You don't want to be a slave.

A chariot, drawn by a pair of sleek, white horses, charges to the foot of the steps, and Pharaoh jumps in.

"In here. What are you waiting for?" he shouts at you. Your foot has no more than touched the chariot when the driver lashes at the horses with his whip. The chariot tears off down the street, with you hanging on for dear life.

On the plain outside the city, an army is hurriedly assembling. "After them! Follow me!" Pharaoh shouts to his general, and then you are off again, hurtling down the desert road, with sand in your hair, grit in your teeth, and dust in your eyes.

The ride seems to go on endlessly. Your arms ache with the effort of hanging on. You are surprised the horses haven't dropped long ago. They are sweating furiously. You camp briefly for the night, and then you're off for another day of mad chase.

At last Pharaoh's driver pulls up on the reins, and the mad flight is halted. You are on the crest of a plateau, looking into the sunset at a valley filled with people and animals. Beyond the people is a large body of water.

"We've got them now, trapped between the mighty Egyptian army and the Red Sea!" the Pharaoh exults. "Let's just see their God get them out of this!"

Pharaoh steps out of his chariot and strides off to confer with his generals.

Choices: **You stay in the chariot and wait for him (turn to page 119).**
You sneak down into the valley, to the Israelite camp (turn to page 113).

When the procession has gone around the city seven times, the marchers stop.

"What now? Do we get a concert on the rams' horns?" someone on the wall shouts.

The priests raise their trumpets to their lips and blow a great blast. Then all the marchers surrounding the city of Jericho give a great shout. You and Chris shout with them at the top of your lungs.

All of a sudden, the ground begins to tremble. There is a roaring sound like an earthquake. People on the wall begin to shriek and wail. The wall teeters. People are flung off.

The mighty walls of the great city of Jericho crumble to the ground, and the army of Israel enters triumphantly.

And you are at the head of it! Chris is impressed. God has done what he promised Joshua.

THE END

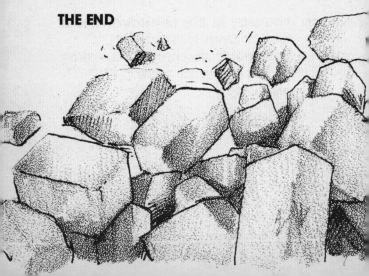

You clamber back into the machine. It lurches and rolls a few times as the ship rides the waves, but finally Chris gets AL set to fly you out of there.

"So, do you want to try for Rome again?" you ask. "You could reset the dials a little bit."

Chris grins. "Yeah, I'd like to. I've had enough of sailing. But I'm not so sure it'll work. How about if we went someplace else instead, to another big city, like Jerusalem?"

Choices: **You cast your vote for going to Rome (turn to page 71).**
You decide you'd like to see Jerusalem (turn to page 51).

You open the time machine door, expecting to be met by the glare of the sun. Instead you find total darkness. It's darker than night, for you see no stars or moon.

"Oh, no. What'd you set this thing for? Are we back in the plagues again?

"Well, I told AL A.D. 67."

You are about to suggest that he try another button when you see some flickering lights.

The lights are small lanterns being carried by a group of people. Now you can see that it's dark because you are in some kind of tunnel or cave.

"Peace, brothers." The leader of the group greets you with an outstretched hand. "I am Honorius. What is it you seek here, deep in the catacombs?"

That explains it. You are in Rome, after all. You know that many of the early Christians used these underground tombs for burials and to hide from persecution.

A young man standing next to the leader is carrying a walking stick. He casually makes a mark in the dirt floor like this: ⌒ . You know what it means and respond by stooping down and finishing the sign with your finger: ⊂✕ . The fish was the secret signal among early Christians, to identify one another. If the other half of the sign went uncompleted, it was only a mark in the dust, nothing to cause anyone to be thrown to the lions. . . .

Turn to page 72.

The others who have hung back in fear now crowd around you in greeting.

"We are just gathering for a memorial service," Honorius says. "Won't you join us?"

You nod, but you feel a little awkward. You follow Honorius down the dim tunnels, with recesses and niches carved out of stone to hold bodies. He stops at a spot where several tunnels intersect to make a large open area. Some others in the group use their lanterns to light torches hanging in brackets on the walls, and soon the room is brightly lit.

The service is like no funeral you've ever attended. The group sings hymns that sound something like psalms. You and Chris try to follow along, but the melodies aren't like any you're used to. After the singing, various members of the group rise to speak of the Christian who was put to death as part of the emperor Nero's persecution of Christians. It turns out that the young man died the year before, thrown to the lions in the Colosseum because he refused to curse the name of Christ. The Christians are using the anniversary of his death as an occasion to celebrate his entry into heaven.

It seems odd to you to celebrate someone's deathday, and you whisper that to the person next to you, a young man named Lucullus.

"Death is not a thing of sadness to us, for it takes us to the Lord," Lucullus says. "That is one reason we meet here. But another reason is that all Romans regard tombs as sacred places. We can meet here without fear of our enemies."

You are amazed at what these people go through for their faith in God. You think of your comfortable life at home. In comparison, you've got it easy.

One person several of the believers mention is a man named Paul, who is in prison in Rome. Paul? You know him. He wrote all those letters that are now books in the Bible! You'd like to see him, but if he's in prison that's probably a dangerous idea.

The service goes on. The Roman Christians take Communion and eat a meal together, and invite you to join them. Then Honorius calls for everyone's attention.

"My brothers, it is time again for us to take food to our brother Paul in prison. It is a dangerous task, but one we gladly perform for him. Who wishes to go this time?"

Next to you, Lucullus speaks up. "I will go."

"Anyone else?" Honorius asks. "Lucullus should not go alone."

You and Chris look at each other.

Choices: **You volunteer to go with Lucullus, in spite of the danger** (turn to page 100)**.**

You decide to explore the catacombs a bit instead (turn to page 77)**.**

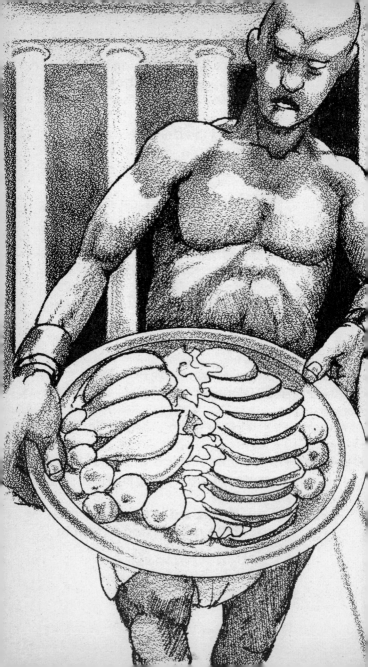

You notice there's no blood around this door as you slip into the party behind two couples. One woman is wearing a gold headdress that covers her forehead, flares out at the side rather like wings, and has a row of glittering jewels over the top. The other is wearing a necklace that extends out on her shoulders like a collar, made of heavy gold and set with stones. The women and the men wear white linen. The men's costumes look like knee-length skirts.

You poke Chris. This should be some party.

The room you enter is huge. The ceiling is supported by pillars painted with gold, red, and turquoise geometric patterns. Slaves in loincloths walk among the guests, passing trays of cakes, fruit, cheeses, and meats.

"Mmmm, taste these cakes," Chris recommends. "You won't believe how sweet they are!"

You take one when the slave offers it to you. It makes you thirsty. Slaves are also offering goblets of drinks. You take one.

Some kind of weird fruit juice. Sour tasting. It makes you sleepy.

You follow some guests up the wide marble stairs and out onto the roof. There are big, puffy cushions and thick rugs all around. The night air is heavy and warm.

Choices: You curl up on a cushion and sleep (turn to page 90).
You go back to the party (turn to page 80).

There aren't many gates in the great wall, and the ones you do find are bolted shut. You spot some vines growing over the edge of the wall. Maybe you could climb them. You stand on Chris's shoulders and reach as high as you can.

All you get for your efforts are scraped knuckles.

"Guess if we want in, we'll have to fly," you say, jokingly.

"Think we can do it?" Chris is serious. And he's right. The professor said the machine could fly like a helicopter or something.

"It's worth a try. This scene is pretty interesting."

You run back to the time machine and set the cartograph screen. "OK, a couple hundred feet up and forward ought to do it." Chris types in the information, then pushes a button.

The next time you open the door, you are inside the city. "Pretty fancy flying," you say. Chris looks as surprised and pleased as you feel.

Outside the wall you hear the sound of the marchers. "Come on. They're coming this way."

You are about to climb to a vantage point on the wall when you see a house with a red rope hanging out the window. You wonder what it's for.

Choices: You go on up the wall (turn to page 83).
You go to the house with the red cord (turn to page 91).

A young girl volunteers to go with Lucullus to buy provisions for Paul. When you tell Lucullus that you'd like to look around the catacombs a bit, he loans you his lantern. He also gives you a warning. "Don't go too far," he says. "There are a number of levels and passageways, and you could get lost. And it could be a long while before anyone found you."

You promise to be careful. Then you and Chris head down one of the corridors, examining the artwork on the walls and the inscriptions by the tombs. The bodies seem to have been stored in recesses on the stone shelves, then covered with slabs of stone. Unfortunately, the translators around your necks can't decipher handwriting, so you don't know what the tomb inscriptions say. But you are able to make out some Roman-sounding names: Flavius, Marcellus, Julia.

All of a sudden you realize that you've wandered farther than you meant to.

"Let's just stay calm," you say to Chris, as you try to remember what turns you made in your exploration of the tombs.

"Calm?" Chris's voice is panicky. "We're lost in an underground cemetery with a bunch of corpses. What if they don't want us here? What if they haunt us?"

Choices: You start to wonder about the corpses (turn to page 84).
You tell Chris not to be afraid of ghosts (turn to page 94).

As you wander around the city, you don't have far to look for food. Everywhere you see open braziers with meat roasting over the flames. "The smell of all this is sure making me hungry."

"Well, there's a family with so many kids they probably wouldn't even notice two more mouths," Chris says.

You approach the doorway, which seems to be overflowing with children running in and out. But there's no need to sneak or try to get lost in the crowd. As soon as they see you, there are hearty invitations to take a meal with them.

You take your place near the end of the table with some of the younger children. "Did you see Jesus ride into town today?" one asks you as you take a bite of bread.

"We sure did!" Chris answers for you.

"We have long awaited the coming of the Promised One," the father says. "Now he will help us march against the Romans."

"Freedom from Roman slavery!" cries the oldest son, banging his fist against the table.

"Are you sure that's what Jesus has in mind?" You grope for the right words. "I mean, he talks about loving your enemies, not about going to war. He even says to pay taxes to Caesar."

"Of course," the son replies heatedly. "Do you think he's going to reveal his real plan to the officials before he's crowned? Certainly not! It'll happen this week — just you wait and see. He'll be crowned king of the Jews. And we'll all be behind him."

You don't want to start an argument, but you

feel uneasy about the conversation. "I'm not so sure . . ." you begin.

"Young man, don't you know the prophets?" The father glares at you. "Daniel said that God would set up a kingdom that would crush all other kingdoms. The Messiah will crush Rome!"

The conversation turns to family topics, but you are uncomfortable. As soon as you can, you and Chris thank your host and hostess and slip out to explore the city. As you walk, you spot a beautiful white building atop a hill. "The Temple!" you exclaim. "Let's go see it."

The gate of the Temple seems to be a public gathering place by day and night. You and Chris look around a bit, then find a spot along the wall where the stones hold the heat of the day and curl up to sleep.

You must have been more tired than you realized. The next thing you know, the sun is beating down on you warmly and there is a big commotion behind you in the Temple courtyard.

Turn to page 110.

"I see some kids our age," Chris says. "Let's go get acquainted."

When you approach the group of young people, you are greeted with a lot of curious stares and some pretty difficult questions.

"Hello. Who are you?" "I've never seen you around here before."

"Yeah, we're new," you say.

"Where did you come from?" Your questioner is suddenly suspicious. "You aren't one of those Hebrews, are you?"

You and Chris shake your heads violently.

A girl with thick, dark hair, parted in the middle and cut straight just above her shoulders, giggles. "Then why are you dressed so funny?"

You and Chris stammer a bit. "Well, we're from a land in the west. We've traveled a long way to learn of Egypt."

The tallest of the boys, who seems to be the leader of the group, steps forward. He is wearing a linen loincloth like the older men in the room, and because he's not wearing a headdress, you can see that his head is shaved bald. "Well then, you must be very tired and dusty," he says. "But that can be easily remedied." He claps his hands and two enormous black slaves appear from nowhere and bow to him.

"My friends have just completed a long journey, and wish to be bathed and dressed for the party."

"Yes, master." The Nubian slaves bow again.

You and Chris look at each other wide-eyed. Bathed? The slaves take you by the arm and lead you firmly from the room into a chamber smelling heavily of oil and spices. You had expected something like a Roman bath, a sort of marble swimming pool. Instead you are presented with large urns of oil. The slaves bow and depart.

"Whew! I thought they were going to bathe us," you say.

"I think we'd better rub some of this stuff on our arms or something, so they won't think they have to help," Chris suggests.

"Yeah, but it stinks—yuck!"

You are only getting started on the process when the Nubians return, bearing clean linen garments for you.

"Where will we hide the translators in those?" whispers Chris.

"I think we'd better make a run for it," you whisper back.

Just then another servant enters, even taller than the first two. He holds something in his hand, very shiny and very sharp. "What's he gonna do? Slit our throats?" Chris asks.

When you see what the slave has in mind, you almost wish he'd slit your throat instead.

"Shave my head?" you yelp.

"All young Egyptian gentlemen have their heads shaved," the slave says placidly. Your scalp tickles under his razor, and the top of your head feels cool. "But I'm not an Egyptian gentleman," you protest.

Turn to page 82.

Chris is no help at all. He stands there laughing.

The slave smiles as if he didn't hear all this, and finishes his job. At least he's good at it — there are no nicks on your skin.

Now Chris quits laughing. It's his turn. The slave completes his job, bows, and departs.

You look around. You're alone. "Let's run!" you say.

You arrive back at the capsule, breathless. Chris starts to work with AL.

"Wait a minute," you say. "We can't go back like this. What'll we say?"

"Yeah. You've got a point there." Then your friend grins mischievously and points to your skull. "And there, and there, and . . ."

You don't think it's funny.

Chris quiets down. "Well, I suppose we could say we're going out for the swim team — you know, less water resistance?"

THE END

By the time you are up on the wall and have elbowed through the spectators to find a good view, the marchers have stopped.

The people around you are laughing and pointing at the people down below. It's like being at the circus.

But all of a sudden it's not entertaining anymore. There is a blast of trumpets, and a great shout from the marchers encircling the wall. You feel the stones beneath you tremble, then shake, then crumble. You're falling. . . .

THE END

Just thinking about the hundreds of dead bodies around you is pretty weird. You start to get prickly feelings up your spine.

"What's that?" Chris whispers.

"What?"

"I thought I heard something."

You feel chills again, and you strain your ears. Then you hear something, too—a plopping sound. . . .

With a shriek, Chris is off down a passageway, and you're hot on his heels, running from an unknown danger into a known one: the trackless maze of the catacombs.

THE END

Crowds of people follow Jesus through the streets of Jerusalem, but as he and his disciples go out the gates in the wall, few people follow. The gates will soon be closing for the night, and no one wants to be shut outside.

The air is getting cooler as evening comes on, a pleasant relief from the heat you endured earlier. It's not a long walk to Bethany. Jesus and his disciples, who are used to walking everywhere, cover the two-mile distance quickly. You and Chris have to run a bit to keep up. You are hoping to hear Jesus tell some parables, but he is silent. He seems to have a lot on his mind.

As you approach a large house in Bethany, you see servants run ahead to spread word of your arrival. At the garden gate, a tall, well-dressed woman hurries forward followed by a younger girl and a handsome young man.

"Master, we have been awaiting you. The feast is all prepared."

"Thank you, Martha. I knew you would have everything ready. Hello, Mary. Hello, Lazarus." Jesus greets each one as they go in.

You tug at Chris's sleeve. "Hey, I know who that is. That's Lazarus, the one Jesus brought back from the dead!"

Chris's eyes open wide with amazement. "Really?"

"Yeah. Lazarus was Jesus' special friend. When he died, it was three days before Jesus finally got here, so no one thought he could help him then."

"But he did anyway?"

"He went to the tomb and said, 'Lazarus, come forth,' and Lazarus did."

Chris shakes his head. "He looks healthy now."

You enter a large hall lit with torches and hung with tapestries. A long table fills the center of the room. Seated around the table on low benches and cushions are Jesus and his disciples, and apparently many of their friends from Bethany. Lazarus sits next to Jesus, talking to him earnestly. Martha is directing the servants, who are busily passing platters laden with tantalizing meats, beautiful fruit, and plump, yellow cheeses. You don't see Mary anywhere.

"Bring in the bread baskets, quickly!" Martha points at you. Realizing you probably look just like one of the many young servants rushing about, you slip through the door to where Martha pointed. When you return with a large basket of hot bread in your arms, you find the room has suddenly become quiet. You stand still, waiting. Then you see what everyone is looking at.

Turn to page 88.

Mary is on her knees near Jesus. She holds a carved white box. You see her break the seal on the box, remove a small glass vial, and break open the vial. A sweet, spicy fragrance fills the room: perfume. Mary pours it on Jesus' head and feet. Then she loosens her long hair. There are gasps of surprise as she kneels down and dries Jesus' feet with her tresses.

The shocked silence is broken by an angry voice from one of Jesus' followers. "This is not a gesture of love. It's a repulsive act of waste! That perfume was worth a fortune!"

Another voice in the room seems to agree. "It must have cost three hundred denarii!"

The first man speaks again. "Think of that! Three hundred denarii! One denarius is a day's wage for a laborer. The perfume should have been sold and the money given to the poor."

Jesus turns to Mary and places his hand on her head. "Why do you trouble the woman, Judas? Mary has done a beautiful thing. You will always have the poor with you, and whenever you wish you can do good for them. But you will not always have me."

Judas does not answer this, but storms from the room, his anger billowing like his robes from behind him. You have the feeling that this quarrel involves more than you just heard.

The dinner guests return uneasily to their food.

Choices: You stay at the feast (turn to page 104).

You follow Judas (turn to page 95).

"Chris, wake up!" You shake your friend, who is still asleep beside you. It's morning, and the party is over. Really over. You hear people weeping and wailing inside the house.

"Something's wrong. Let's get out of here."

You see a stairway that leads off the balcony and into the backyard. There is a wall around the yard, but you think you can climb it.

You are almost over the wall when you are spotted. A servant grabs you and hauls you roughly into the house.

"I found these foreigners sneaking over the wall, master." He shoves you to your knees in front of a fierce-looking Egyptian. A woman is sitting next to him, wailing loudly.

"And what do you know about this?" The Egyptian demands. He points to a pallet in the corner of the room, where a handsome young boy seems to be sleeping.

"My firstborn son," the father says. Then he begins to weep, too. "You have killed him!" he shouts.

Your mouth drops open, and you look wildly at Chris. He starts struggling with the servant, but it is no use. You are dragged off. It seems to be
THE END.

Just as all the houses on this side of the street, this house is built into the wall of the city. It doesn't look any different from the other houses in the row. They're all sandy colored and square in shape. The red rope hanging out the upper story window is its only distinguishing mark.

You knock on the wooden door. "So what do we say if anyone answers?" Chris asks.

You're not sure either, but you don't have long to worry about it. The door is opened almost immediately by a pretty woman in a rose colored robe with white ribbons entwined in her hair.

Before you can speak, two women in the street stop and speak to you sharply. "You young men get away from there. That's not a proper place for children," says one.

"Don't you know? That's the house of Rahab!" says the other.

Then they gather their robes around them and hurry on down the street.

You turn to look at the face of the woman in the doorway. She doesn't look evil to you, but you know appearances can be deceiving.

Choices: **You decide to enter this house despite the warning (turn to page 98).**
You go to the wall to look at the view (turn to page 83).

You and Chris step out of the time machine and rub your eyes. You are in the middle of a great army camp. Tents are pitched all around you. The men everywhere are busy, shining their spears and shields, mending their tents, cooking food. Three men walk by you with empty water flasks.

"Here, you!" one of them orders roughly. "Run down to the well with these and fill them with water for us."

He thrusts the flasks into your hands and points off to the right. Fortunately, you spot a well. "And be quick about it," he growls.

You and Chris hurry to the large, rock-encircled well and wait until several others have finished drawing their water. You have just filled the flasks you carry when you hear a trumpet blast. Apparently it was a signal for the men to get quiet, because everyone does. You look to the center of the camp and see the leader, a mighty-looking man with strong muscles showing beneath his dark brown tunic and leather armor.

"Men of Israel," he calls. "The Lord God has spoken to me. He said, 'The people with you are too many for me to give them a victory over the Midianites. For then Israel might boast of its own power, saying that our own hands have saved us.'"

The men around you start shaking their heads and murmuring to each other. "What's he talking about?" "Doesn't Gideon realize we're already outnumbered three to one?"

Now you know the leader's name is Gideon.

He holds up his hands for silence.

"The Lord God has said to me, 'Go to the people, therefore, and tell everyone who is fearful and afraid to go back, and leave Mount Gilead.' "

There is a great turmoil in the camp. The men whose water flasks you carry run up and grab them. They are great, strong soldiers. If they're getting out while the getting's good, maybe they know something you don't.

"Should we stay?" you ask Chris.

Turn to page 102.

"Come on, Chris," you say. "You don't believe in ghosts, do you?"

"Why shouldn't I?" he says. "How do you know they aren't real?"

"Well," you admit, "I do know that the Bible says there are such things as evil spirits that serve the devil. I don't know about ghosts. But I do know that I don't have to be afraid of them."

"Why not?" Chris is curious.

"Because I believe in God. And God is stronger than any evil being. I know he'll protect me," you explain.

Your words calm Chris down a bit, and, by concentrating, the two of you are able to find your way back to the band of Christians. You ask Honorius to take you back to where he first found you. He looks puzzled at your request.

"It's just that we—we left something there," you explain. You see no point in adding that what you left was an invisible time machine!

Soon you and Chris are back in AL. "I hear it's kind of a long walk to Rome," you say. "We could fly AL over there."

"Well, my friend," Chris replies, "I'd also be interested in trying to find the Jesus these people were talking about."

Choices: You fly AL into Rome to find Lucullus (turn to page 149).
You ask AL to take you to Jerusalem in Jesus' time (turn to page 51).

Judas has a head start on you, and his anger and long legs carry him at a fast pace. The trip from Bethany to Jerusalem is a long way to run, but that's what you do. You arrive at the city wall just behind Judas. The sun is setting, and the huge gates are being shut and barred for the night. But there is a small door beside the gate.

Judas pounds on the gate until the gatekeeper opens a window. "What do you want?" he growls in a surly voice.

"Let me in. I have business!" Judas barks back.

"Who are you?"

"Judas Iscariot. I have business with the High Priest. It's important."

"All right." The gatekeeper unbolts the heavy gate and opens it just a little. "You shouldn't try to come in after sundown. Those are your servants, are they?"

Judas turns and seems to see you for the first time, "What are you two doing here? Didn't I see you at Martha's house? Has she sent you to follow me?" He seems to do everything angrily.

"No, sir. We aren't really her servants. We just followed Jesus in — we wanted to know what was going on."

"Well, you can't come with me. And I don't want you sneaking around following me, either."

You nod, but you don't intend to obey him.

Turn to page 132.

You don't know how long you slept, but you're awakened abruptly.

"Gather your possessions," says the Hebrew boy. "We must leave, quickly!"

You do as he says. The Hebrew family has already packed their essential goods: a kneading trough for making bread, a few other cooking utensils, cloaks and sleeping mats, and dry foodstuffs such as grains, yeast, and salt.

The only thing you want to pack is the time machine, but now you're not even sure you can find it. You left it near that wealthy home.

The Hebrew family hurries you out into the street, where you see people moving flocks of sheep and goats, and herds of cattle. It looks like rush hour, except that it's still dark. One of the children in your Hebrew family comes rushing up carrying gold jewelry and several pouches of copper rings. "The Egyptians want us to go away so much that they gave us these!" she exclaims.

"Somehow it all seems too good to be true," Chris mutters to you as you trudge east with the throng. "It's hard to believe the Egyptians would just let all these slaves go. I have a feeling we haven't seen the last of them."

You have a feeling he's right.

Choices: You stay with the departing slaves (turn to page 105).
You work your way against traffic, find the time machine, and go elsewhere (turn to page 51).

The women's words are still ringing in your ears, embarrassing you, but the woman in front of you is calm and poised.

"I am Rahab, mistress of this house. What can I do for you?"

"Well, we're visitors here, you see and we—uh, we . . ." You stammer and stutter, wondering just what it is that you do want to ask.

"I think I understand. You are visitors to our city, and you find it under siege by the Hebrews. Do come in."

You step inside. The coolness of the shady room is refreshing. Even this early in the morning, it is hot out in the streets.

"Why did you choose my door to knock on?"

"Well, we saw the red rope," you explain. "I guess it looked sort of welcoming."

Rahab starts to answer, but is interrupted by a tumult of noise: trumpets, shouting, shrieking. The house is shaking and the crashing of tumbling rocks is deafening. Is it an earthquake?

You rush to the window with Rahab and her family. Everywhere you see rubble and bodies. The great wall of the city of Jericho looks like a pile of children's building blocks—very large children, at that. The army that had been marching around the city is now swarming over the rubble to do battle. Strangely, the portion of the wall you're lodged in is still standing. You look at your hostess in wonder.

"It is just as the men said it would be!" Rahab is exclaiming. "You see, some time ago I rented a room to two Hebrew men. I had heard many things about the Hebrews and the mighty God they worship. The king of Jericho heard that these men were at my house, and asked me to turn them over to him as spies. But I hid them instead.

"Later that night I helped them escape out my window by letting them climb down this red rope. They told me that they would come back, and that if I left this red cord in the window, anyone in the house with me would be safe. And it all came true. Their God is surely very powerful. And he kept me safe."

It is all very confusing to you. "But those things the women said in the street . . ." You don't know quite how to ask your question.

Rahab smiles. "You are wondering why the Hebrew God should spare the life of a woman with a bad reputation. It is a mystery to me also. But I do know one thing. The Lord God of the Israelites is the true God!"

You have to agree with Rahab that the evidence is pretty overwhelming.

Choices: You've had enough adventure for now, and decide to go home (turn to page 146).
You take AL elsewhere (turn to page 92).

"We will go with Lucullus," you say to Honorius. "We would like to see Paul."

Honorius smiles. Then he hands a small pouch of coins to Lucullus. "This is not much, but it is all the money we have. If you go to the shopkeeper on the Appian Way who is a believer, he may give you more food at his own cost."

The two of you follow Lucullus up some stairs and out of the underground tombs. The bright sunlight dazzles you. "This is the Appian Way," Lucullus says proudly. "We have a little distance to walk on it. You see, we're outside Rome itself. No tombs are allowed inside the city limits."

The Appian Way is a beautiful, wide boulevard, well-paved and lined with tall trees on both sides. The three of you walk along the edge of the road, well out of the way of the chariots dashing in both directions.

You are tired and thirsty by the time you arrive at the shop a couple of miles later. A little old man, stoop-shouldered and baldheaded, emerges from the shadows in the back. Lucullus begins to tell him what you need. As he talks, he picks up a stylus and doodles in the dust on the shop counter. One of his doodles is a fish.

The old man's wrinkled face breaks into a broad smile. "I'll be most happy to fill your order." He begins busily filling baskets. Soon you and Chris have plenty to carry. While Lucullus tells the little shopkeeper good-bye, you step out into the street.

There is a clanking metallic sound as a heavy hand clutches your shoulder. "Aha, just as my commander thought. This shop is a supplier for Christians. Who gave you the money, boy? And where are the friends you are taking this food to?"

"What? We don't know what you mean," you stammer, stalling for time. Lucullus, you hope, can slip out the back door of the little shop.

"Don't try to tell me all this is just for your family, boy. Don't try to lie to Claudius of Caesar's legions. You are a Christian!"

Choices: **You say, "You're crazy" (turn to page 108).**
You say, "Yes, Jesus Christ is my Lord" (turn to page 109).

You decide to stay. Now you're hungry, and lots of the men have left so quickly that their cook pots are still sitting by their fires. You and Chris find one that smells like a pretty good stew.

"Mmmm, not too bad," you say, sampling a mouthful.

"Meat's kinda tough," says Chris. "Wonder what's in here?"

You think it's probably just as well you don't know, but you eat a bowlful anyway. Then you both crawl into the bedding that the soldiers also abandoned. The woven blankets are scratchy and the animal skins smell a bit, but you're tired and you both sleep well.

The next morning you heat up some more of that stew for breakfast. You'd rather have corn-flakes, but even if there were such a thing around you'd probably have to eat them with goat's milk, so never mind!

You've just finished breakfast when Gideon again calls the men to attention. "Men of Israel, last night a count was taken. Twenty-two thousand men returned home. Ten thousand brave warriors remain with us." Some men cheer; others look frightened when they hear the numbers.

Gideon silences the men. "This morning the Lord God of Israel again spoke to me, and said, 'There are still too many people. Bring them down to the water, and I will test them for you.' Men of Israel—to the river!"

It sounds good to you. You're thirsty after a breakfast of salty stew, anyway. When you get to the riverbanks you wonder what the test is. You have a vague feeling there's something important about how you drink, but you can't remember the Bible story that well, so you just drink.

Choices: **You lie down and lap the water like a dog (turn to page 114).**
You kneel and cup your hands (turn to page 130).

The guests have all been served and are lounging contentedly around the table, talking quietly as the lamps burn low. In the kitchen you and Chris and the other servants have eaten and are beginning the work of cleaning up.

"Martha is a good cook," Chris comments.

"The best in Bethany," a servant girl sitting near you says proudly. "She's famous for her hospitality. The Master comes here often."

Just then Martha herself enters the kitchen. "You have done a superb job tonight—really outdone yourselves. The Master was pleased and I am so proud of you." She smiles at the servants, who return to their work. Martha comes to you and Chris. "I don't recall hiring you. Have you worked here before?"

"Ah, no," you stammer. "We're travelers. We were just sort of helping out tonight."

"Well, you were needed. Why don't you spend the night here before you go on to Jerusalem?"

You look at Chris. Chris nods.

You must have been more tired than you realized, because the next thing you know the sun is beating down warmly on you and your bed mat on Martha's roof.

Chris's mat is empty, but soon he returns. "We slept in," he says sheepishly. "Jesus left already."

The two of you thank Martha and hurry to Jerusalem to find Jesus. You think the Temple might be a good spot to start looking.

Turn to page 110.

With the crowd you walk and walk. At night you camp out under the stars. Your journey takes you from watered fields to a vast desert. You finally stop one evening by the banks of a large body of water.

There is no way to cross. And when you look back across the desert, you see a dark, moving mass silhouetted against the sunset. Chris's prediction just may have come true: you may not have seen the last of the Egyptians. . . .

Turn to page 113.

Inside the city, you run up the street to talk to two women. "There's something you should know! We want to give you a warning!" The women turn and look at you like you're crazy.

"Listen!" You're talking fast and almost yelling. "Did you know there's an army out there? This city is surrounded. And soon the walls will fall. You should do something to protect yourselves!"

"You must mean crazy Joshua and his merry marchers," one woman answers. "Don't worry about them. And these walls will never fall! So run along, boys."

The women walk on. You see five or six children playing a game on the other side of the street.

"Hey, don't you kids have a safer place to play? There's an enemy army out there? There could be trouble anytime."

The kids shrug and laugh. A little girl with big brown eyes says, "Of course, silly, everybody knows that. They've been there all week."

"But, that's the point. . . ."

You never get to finish your sentence. You hear a blaring noise of trumpets from the other side of the wall, and then everything is drowned in the sound of shattering stone and tumbling rubble.

"Where's AL?"

"Look out! That roof's falling!"

"Down this street, hurry!"

Through the falling rock and frenzied screams, you and Chris race for the safety of the machine.

THE END

"You're lying!" The Roman soldier strikes you across the side of your head and you reel backwards, spilling the baskets of provisions all over the ground.

As if by magic, a dozen ragged children dart from nowhere and begin scrambling in the dirt for the food you have dropped. Your mind is fuzzy from the blow, but you are coherent enough to think that at least the food won't be wasted. These children are starving.

"The next time you lie to a Roman legionnaire you won't get off so easily," Claudius growls at you. Then he marches off.

Chris helps you up, and you wonder what to do next. You're too ashamed to go back to your Christian friends. You have no more money to buy food for Paul, but if you tell them what happened they'll know you denied Jesus. You could never face them with that.

You see a loaf of bread under a bush that the beggar children missed. You pick it up, dust it off, break it in half, and hand a piece to Chris. He takes it, but doesn't eat much.

"Feel up to exploring Rome a bit?" you ask. You don't think this is a very good time to mention to Chris that you don't know how you'll ever get back to the time machine.

Turn to page 142.

You stand there shaking after your bold testimony. But before your very eyes the hard lines on Claudius's face soften, and he lowers his spear.

"Take me with you."

"No!" It was bad enough to think you would be tortured yourself, but now he's demanding that you endanger Paul further, or betray your Christian friends. That's unthinkable.

"You don't understand. I promise by the life of Caesar I won't betray them or you. I want to know the truth for myself."

You look helplessly at Chris. What should you do? Claudius seems sincere. But if you're wrong, the whole band of Christians could be killed.

Choices: You say, "All right, come with me" (turn to page 111).

You say, "I don't believe you" (turn to page 120).

110

The courtyard of the Temple is as busy as a marketplace—not the holy, reverent atmosphere you'd expect to find.

"Doves, pure white turtledoves. A special on the pair!" one merchant calls to the crowd.

"Change your money, my young friends? Best exchange rate you'll find in Jerusalem." A man with a long sharp nose and dirty hair beckons to you and Chris.

You turn a corner around some stalls containing sheep and goats and see what caused the noise that wakened you. A man with his back to you is angrily knocking over tables of coins and shouting at the money changers. Apparently he has cleared out other stalls before these, because there are lambs and goats running around loose. The bleating animals add to the confusion of angry cries and shouts of people scrambling for the coins spilled all over the courtyard.

The man in the center of it all seizes a whip from a table and begins driving the merchants before him. As he turns, you see who it is. Jesus!

"I think your Jesus has gone crazy! Somebody should do something!" yells Chris. He starts running toward the Temple's inner court.

Choices: You run into the inner court with Chris (turn to page 116).
You stop him (turn to page 121).

Your instincts tell you Claudius is sincere. You think you'll take him to the catacombs instead of to the prison. Then even if he's a spy, he will be greatly outnumbered and your friends will know the catacombs far better than he could.

"You'll have to leave your weapons here," you say.

He takes a dagger out of his belt and leans his spear against the wall of the shop. Soon you are on your way. You think it must be a strange sight for a Roman legionnaire to be walking along the Appian Way with two basket-laden kids, but no one pays any attention to you.

You don't go very far into the catacombs when you are met by Honorius, Lucullus, and several of the Christian band. They see Claudius. "Oh, no! A Roman guard!" "What is he doing here?" "We've been betrayed!" A girl begins to weep.

Claudius holds out his hands. "Do not fear. It's true that I am under orders to search out Christians and to have them arrested. But I really want to know what your religion is all about. Daily I watch Christians die so bravely in the Colosseum. I want to know more about this God you serve."

There is a moment of shocked silence.

Then Honorius speaks. "Come with us, my son. We will be glad to speak of our faith with you." He leads Claudius away. Already they are talking intensely.

Turn to page 112.

112

You and Chris borrow Lucullus's lantern again, this time to light your way back to the time capsule. As you go, you think how strange it is that you should feel sad about leaving this dismal place. Your steps become slower and slower.

"They sure are neat people," you say wistfully.

"Yeah. I was thinking the same thing."

"We don't really have to go yet."

"What if they miss us at home?"

"Professor Quinten could explain to our folks."

Choices: You decide to go back home (turn to page 146).
You stay (turn to page 117).

The man who seems to be the leader of the former slaves climbs up onto a mound of earth to speak. But the people don't let him. Everyone seems to be angry. You press forward to the front of the group.

"What's the matter, Moses? Weren't there enough graves in Egypt for us, so you had to bring us out into the desert to die?" shouts a man near you.

You hear a woman's voice next. "It would have been better for us to be slaves to the Egyptians than to die in the wilderness!"

Moses holds up his hands. "Do not be afraid!" he shouts. "Just stand still and watch the power of the Lord save you. The Egyptians you see today you will never see again!"

It seems like quite a claim Moses is making, since you're sure the Egyptian army is no slouch outfit. Where is Chris? You wish you could talk this over. What about the machine?

Choices: **You stay with Moses and the Hebrews (turn to page 122).**
You go back among the Egyptians (turn to page 119).

Chris also has lapped the water like a dog, so you are both among the three hundred men to stay with Gideon.

Gideon gives each man a trumpet and an empty pitcher with a light inside.

"I thought he'd issue us swords," Chris says. "These seem like strange battle weapons."

You agree. "He's probably got orders from God again," you add. You just hope the scheme works, whatever it is.

"Now, men of Israel, watch me," Gideon instructs. "When I come to the outskirts of the enemy camp, you do whatever I do. We'll surround them. Then when I blow on my trumpet, you blow, too, and shout, 'The sword of the Lord and of Gideon!' "

You have been divided into groups of one hundred men each. Your group is sent to the far side of the camp. Since it's the middle of a very dark night, the going is rough. You keep stumbling over rocks and bumping into the other men in the dark. You're afraid you'll drop your pitcher, or hurt yourself and cry out. No one needs to tell you that silence is helpful in a sneak attack.

Finally everyone is in place. The valley seems perfectly still and sleeping. No dark figures move in the shadows. Only Midianite guards pace in their set pattern around the camp.

Suddenly the peace of the night is shattered as the first trumpet peals out. Soon you and the three hundred trumpets blast forth, tearing the sleeping army from their tents. When the Midianites emerge from the blackness of their shelter, their eyes are blinded as Gideon's men break the pitchers that have been shielding torches within. The stirring cries of "The sword of the Lord and of Gideon!" echo over and over.

In the enemy camp, the terrified soldiers stampede to escape. In the confusion they draw their swords on one another, killing many of their own men as they flee.

All this time the army of Gideon stands — every man in his place. As the first red and gold streaks of sunrise appear in the sky, Gideon gives a mighty shout of triumph. "The victory is the Lord's!"

You'd say that was a pretty accurate description of the battle.

THE END

Four men are standing inside the Temple's inner court. All are wearing long blue and white robes with jeweled and embroidered shawls. Three of them have long grey beards and scarves with fringes on them.

"There's a man making a mess out there," cries Chris. "Shouldn't you do something to stop him?"

"Yes, my young friend, we intend to. We intend to stop him permanently."

The one without a beard says, "This Jesus is taking over our Temple. I say if we don't get rid of him now it will be too late."

A priest wearing a gold jeweled box around his neck replies, "But there are many who believe he is a prophet. We must plan carefully. Now," he looks back at you, "you say you saw what happened in the courtyard?"

"Yes, sir," you mutter, looking at the ground.

"Fine. You can bear witness for us in court." He turns and mutters something to the others.

"I feel sick," Chris says.

"Yeah, I think we wound up on the wrong side. Let's get out of here!"

When you start to leave the priests send the Temple guards after you. You have a head start, but you don't stop running until you get back to AL. You intend to learn more about this Jesus and Temple and priest stuff in a safer place — in the Bible as soon as you get home.

THE END

You hurry back to the little band of warmth and fellowship with a light heart. As you round the last corner back to the group, you are welcomed by the golden glow of torchlight, the smell of freshly prepared food, and the sweet sound of soft singing. You feel as if you've come home.

Honorius steps forward, grasps your arm, and leads you to the other side of the room. "My children have just joined us. I want you to meet them, as they're about your own age. My daughter, Rhoda." You look into the large, dark eyes of a beautiful girl with long, black hair. She smiles shyly.

"And my son, Felix." A handsome youth with curly brown hair grasps your hand warmly.

At the time you don't understand why you feel so tongue-tied, and why your palms begin to perspire. A few years later, when Honorius becomes your father-in-law, you still haven't forgotten that first meeting with his children.

Neither have you forgotten your friend Chris, who returned to his own time. . . .

THE END

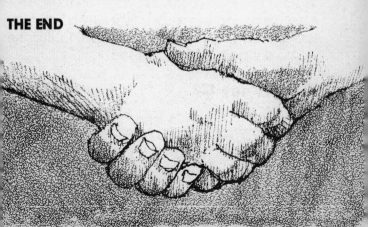

Moses has managed to quiet the people down somehow. Then he stretches out his hand over that body of water. A strong wind begins to blow over the sea. As the night grows darker, the wind howls stronger and stronger. The water begins to be blown aside, leaving a dry path through the middle!

Moses directs the people to begin crossing over the dry seabed. You choke down your amazement and start walking. On both sides of you the water is sticking up like a wall because of the wind. You remember the trip you took to New York City once: this is just like walking down Fifth Avenue, with skyscrapers on each side.

You still don't know where Chris is, and you're starting to get worried. You're also tired. It's been dark for a long time, and you feel like you've been walking all night.

Finally you see red clouds with golden streaks rising from them. Sunrise! In the dawning light, you come out of the seabed onto the shore. Thousands of Hebrews are standing all along the banks.

You turn and see what they're watching: hundreds of Egyptian chariots in hot pursuit, using the same dry path through the sea!

Turn to page 122.

You look around. Pharaoh's troops are like a whirlwind around you: horses and chariots, soldiers with spears and swords, rattling armor, pounding hooves.

You are swept along with them into the middle of the seabed as they pursue the Israelites. "I have a very bad feeling about this," you say to yourself. You wish you'd listened more carefully when your Sunday school teacher read Bible stories. Then you'd know how this was going to end.

All of a sudden, a wave of water crashes over the men and horses all around you. You look up. The wall of water is tumbling down.

"Swim!" you yell, but your voice is drowned in the noise of screaming men and thrashing horses.

THE END

You'll never know what Claudius would have replied to this, because just then he is joined by a fellow guard.

"Good work, Claudius. That makes six Christians we've captured this week. We'll be up for promotion to captain at this rate."

Claudius doesn't look too happy to see his friend, but they march you off.

"It's almost time for the next show. We might as well take them straight to the Colosseum. This is your lucky day, Christian!" He shoves you roughly on the shoulder and laughs. "I hear Emperor Nero is planning to attend. Not everyone gets a chance to perform for the emperor!"

"Don't they get a trial first?" Claudius asks.

"Oh, that." The other guard shrugs. "All right. We can take them to the Temple of Saturn."

Turn to page 124.

"Wait a minute!" You make a dive for Chris and you both land in a heap just outside the Temple door.

Before you can say anything else, Jesus speaks in a clear voice that carries above the tumult. "It is written in the Scriptures that my house shall be called a house of prayer. But you have made it a den of thieves!" Then he continues across the courtyard, ridding it of merchants and animals.

You look at Chris for his reaction to Jesus' statement. Chris is still breathing hard, but not making any moves to run to the priests. It's calmer in the courtyard now, too.

"Now look: there's a bunch of his followers. Let's go see what they do," you say reasonably.

Turn to page 127.

The appearance of the Egyptians doesn't seem to have upset Moses. You see him climb onto a large boulder, then stretch out his arm and wave it over the sea.

Immediately the sea returns to its bed! Those big skyscraper walls come crashing down; they meet each other with a tremendous impact. The Egyptians are lost in the swirling whirlpool that results. Then the waters smooth out, and the sea is calm, as if nothing unusual had happened.

You shudder. God's power, as you've seen it displayed today, is really amazing—and also terrifying. The Egyptians were foolish to oppose the Lord.

Then an awful thought occurs to you. What if Chris was back there with the Egyptians? Frustrated, you kick at a rock you see on the ground, forgetting that you have only sandals on. "Ouch!" You grab your throbbing toe and hop around.

"What's the matter? Hurt yourself?" a familiar voice asks.

"Chris!" You're so glad to see your friend that you forget your toe. "Where have you been? I've looked everywhere!"

"I didn't cross the Red Sea. I ran back to the machine."

"What do you mean you didn't cross? You're here, aren't you?"

Chris winks. "I mean I didn't cross with you guys. I did it the easy way. I flew over. The machine's right here."

You look around, but don't see a thing. Chris

makes a fist and knocks on what seems to be thin air. You hear the sound of metal. AL's invisibility button is on, of course.

"Well, I've had enough of Egypt for a while," Chris says. "What do you want to do next?"

Choices: **You decide to go home, in case your parents are worried about you (turn to page 125).**
Chris says, "Let's have AL take us to a battle" (turn to page 92).

You are led roughly into the very heart of Rome, but you're in no shape to enjoy the sight of the beautiful, stately buildings. The guards drag you into what appears to be a pagan temple, dotted with statues and full of the smell of burning incense.

"You Christians are enemies of the state," the one guard accuses. "Look at all these people. They worship their gods, yet they remain loyal to the emperor. But you—"

You interrupt. "We don't have any problem with obeying the government. Honest, we don't. We can be loyal to the emperor."

The guard bends to look closely into your eyes. "Ah, but you are loyal to your Christ, more than to the emperor. Is that not true?"

Chris looks at you. You look down at the ground.

The guard straightens up again. "If you can curse the name of Christ, we will let you go. We will forget this whole matter."

Chris is looking at you in panic. Claudius is watching you with what seems to be pity and curiosity.

Choices: You deny being a Christian (turn to page 131).
You refuse to curse Christ's name (turn to page 129).

The machine stops its vibrations, and you know you have arrived—somewhere. As always, you open the door prepared for anything. But not for this strange sight. A long, thin face with a shock of black hair and bright, excited eyes pokes in the door before you can get out.

"It worked; it worked! All just as I thought it would!" Professor Q sounds as excited as a little kid.

"Yeah, it worked really great," you and Chris agree. For the next hour you are plied with questions by the professor, and recount your adventures.

"Come back anytime," he calls after you as you and Chris start down the sidewalk. "Anytime at all!"

You look at your watch. "Wow! We were away all that time, and only a couple of hours have passed here. I can't believe it."

"What do you want to do now?" Chris asks.

"I'd like to tell somebody about this! How about the newspapers? We could be famous!"

"Do you think Professor Quinten would mind?"

"I don't know," you say doubtfully. "You know what else? I just remembered: my Sunday school class is planning a hike up Camel's Back this afternoon. We could go on that."

Choices: You call the newspaper (turn to page 133).
You go on the hike (turn to page 137).

Jesus is standing in the center of a crowd outside the Temple. He seems to be engaged in conversation—a question-and-answer session.

As you get close enough to hear, a man says, "Master, tell us: is it right to pay taxes to Caesar?"

Everyone strains to hear Jesus answer. "They've got him now," a man next to you says. "If he says yes, the people will turn against him because they hate to pay taxes to Rome. If he says no, the Romans will arrest him for treason. The priests have worked a long time to trap him."

You hold your breath. You can see the trap. How will Jesus answer?

Turn to page 128.

Jesus asks the questioner for a coin. The man looks surprised, but hands Jesus a silver coin about the size of a dime. Jesus holds it out to him. "Whose picture is on this?" he asks.

The man doesn't even have to look at the coin to answer. "Caesar's," he says and shrugs.

"Then give to Caesar the things that are Caesar's, and to God the things that are God's," Jesus replies.

Most of the crowd murmurs its approval at his wise answer to the question, but you also see some angry scowls.

Just then you see some of Jesus' disciples and others nearby in a heated discussion.

"He missed a perfect opportunity, Judas! Why didn't he declare the Jews free from Roman taxes right now?"

"This man is not the king who will set us free," the man called Judas says scornfully.

"But he said he was! He said he was sent from God. If he's not our king, then he's an impostor!"

"He's an impostor, and he should be turned over to Rome."

"No, no. Don't be so hotheaded, Judas. Maybe he just doesn't realize we're ready to follow him to battle.

"Come on. Some friends of mine are having a meeting about it. You'll see the truth."

**Choices: Follow to see what the militants are planning (turn to page 140).
Stay with Jesus (turn to page 150).**

The words come out of Chris's mouth before you have a chance to say anything. "I—I curse the name of Christ," he says shakily.

"Very well," says the guard. "And what about your friend?"

"I can't do that," you say. "I just can't."

"Then, to the Colosseum with you!" the guard says triumphantly, grabbing you by the shoulder. He shoves Chris away. "You, scum, begone, and consider yourself fortunate that we gave you a chance to see the truth!"

The guard is taking you out of the temple, with Claudius following reluctantly behind, when Chris comes running up to you again. "I don't know why you're doing this," he says, "but I'm going to find Lucullus and learn some more."

It is the last you see of Chris, for the guard shoves him away again.

Turn to page 134.

Because you and Chris both knelt to drink the water with cupped hands, you have been dismissed from Gideon's ranks. There doesn't seem to be much fun in hanging around the empty tents, so you go back to the time machine.

"Hey, what are all those people doing around the time capsule?"

"Oh no — look!"

"What?"

"Look, you can see it! We forgot to push the electronic invisibility button. I think we'd better get to the machine before they do something to it."

You both charge through the crowd in your best soccer pass style and jump in the machine before anyone can stop you.

"Blast off!" yells Chris.

No time to think this out, you just push a button.

Turn to page 144.

You're terrified. You don't want to die. Surely words don't mean anything, you tell yourself.

"I—I curse the name of . . . Christ," you manage to say. Chris says the same thing.

Claudius looks at you with something like pity, the other guard, with contempt.

"Off with you, then, scum," he says, shoving you so hard you fall to the floor of the temple. "Consider yourselves fortunate that we were so kind to you!" Then, with a clatter of armor, the two soldiers are gone.

You get up from the floor shakily. You feel terrible, and it's not just from the bruises those guards gave you.

"Let's get out of here," you mutter to Chris.

Turn to page 142.

Ducking into alleys and behind buildings to avoid Judas's backward glances, you and Chris follow the angry disciple across town.

"Wonder where he's going?" Chris asks.

"I don't know," you reply, "but wherever it is, he isn't very proud of it."

Finally you see Judas knock at the door of a large, impressive home. The person he's meeting with seems to have a lot of power and importance. A servant answers the door and at first seems inclined to turn Judas away. But Judas's whispers eventually succeed in getting him inside.

"Now what do we do?" Chris asks. "We can't follow him."

"Maybe if we look around the outside of the place, we can find a window," you suggest.

After a little searching, you are successful. You and Chris crouch beneath the window and listen for Judas's voice.

Turn to page 140.

"Good afternoon; this is **The Statesman**," a pleasant voice says at the other end of the line.

"Uh, news department, please," you reply.

"One moment." Another line rings.

"Yeah, Davis. News," says a nasal voice. You can almost smell the smoke and ink in the room.

"We've got a real story for you, sir!" You begin telling him about your adventure. You talk so fast your words are tumbling over each other. "And then the professor—"

You pause for breath, and are dismayed to hear loud snorts of laughter on the other end.

"Great, kid! That's great! You've got a million-dollar imagination. But you've got the wrong place here. You want to write a science fiction novel, not a newspaper story."

Click. He hangs up.

You stand there feeling angry and frustrated. Then something dawns on you.

"Hey, Chris! I've got a great idea! We can write a book! I've already got a good title: **Professor Q's Mysterious Machine**."

THE END

The soldier leads you to a huge stone arena called the Colosseum, and puts you in a dungeon area beneath it. You find yourself amid a diverse group of people: Christians, criminals, slaves, prisoners of war. They have one thing in common: they are all going to die, and they have different reactions to that fact. Some are terrified. Some are calm. Some don't really believe it's happening.

But it is. Soon you are led up into the arena. It looks much like a football stadium, and the screaming spectators could almost be a typical sports crowd in the twentieth century. But they have come to watch people die.

When the doors are opened to let in the wild beasts, you feel like you're watching a scene of a movie. You know it'll all be over soon, and you won't regret your decision. God is more important to you than anything.

THE END

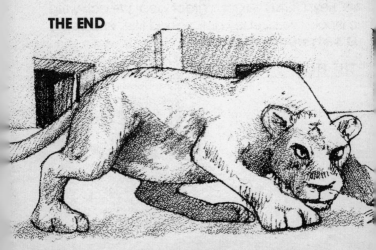

You emerge into the sunlight, and the two of you continue your tour of the streets of Rome. But it seems to have lost some of its dazzle for you. You wonder if you should have let Chris stay with Paul, or try to tell him more about Jesus yourself. But you don't want him to think you are preaching. And you don't really know what to say.

You're thinking so hard that you aren't paying much attention as you start across the street.

Not enough attention. "Look out!" Chris yells. A runaway chariot is careening down the boulevard. You look up just in time to see the slashing feet of two wild horses. The last thing you remember is the frenzied look in their red eyes and the foam slobbering around their bits.

When you come to, you're in the courtyard of a Roman home. Chris is bending over you, and a man is holding a wineskin to your lips.

"Are you all right?" Chris really sounds concerned.

"Yeah, I think so." You rub a painfully skinned elbow. You have a headache.

"You could have been killed," Chris says. "Those hooves just missed you. This man took us into his home so you could recover." Chris leans closer. "Frankly, I don't know where we are anymore. It may take us a while to find AL."

"That's OK." You smile weakly. "There's some stuff I want to tell you in the meantime."

THE END

. All twelve kids from your Sunday school class show up for the hike up the three-mile nature trail, and there are two other visitors besides Chris. Mr. Roames has his hands full. The kids are all excited about Camel's Back, and keep wandering off into the woods.

You and Chris look at each other and shake your heads. Hiking is pretty tame stuff compared to what you've been through today.

You get a real jolt when Mr. Roames calls the kids together for a devotional time on the top of Camel's Back. He's talking about how easy it is to take God's care for granted. His example: the Israelites.

"God subjected Egypt to ten plagues to convince Pharaoh to let the Israelites go," Mr. Roames explained. "So you'd think that the Israelites would realize that God could do anything. But when they got to the Red Sea, they seemed to forget all about God's power, and—"

"The Egyptians didn't just kick them out," you burst out, to Mr. Roames's surprise. "They gave the Hebrews jewelry and the copper rings they used for money!"

Your statement is greeted with shocked silence. Mr. Roames finally speaks up. "Copper rings, you say? That's very interesting. You must have been reading some archaeology books."

"Um, well, I have been more interested in history lately," you manage to say.

THE END

After a pause, Paul says, "You may already be dead, Chris."

Startled, Chris looks down at his arms and legs to make sure he's still there.

Paul smiles. "I mean dead in your sins."

Lucullus breaks into the conversation. "You see, Chris, there are two kinds of people walking around in the world. There are people whose spirits are dead because they are out of contact with God. Their evil has put up a barrier between them and him. And there are people whose spirits are alive, because they have salvation in Jesus. He has torn the curtain separating them from God."

"We don't mean to sound morbid," Paul adds, "but when you receive this new kind of life in Jesus, the old one passes away. It's dead. Gone. That's what I was saying in my letter. And physical

death doesn't really matter. This new kind of life with God goes on forever. After you die, you receive a new body."

"Wow," Chris says. "So that's why so many Christians aren't afraid to die for their belief."

Just then a guard comes in and shoos all the visitors out, including Paul's scribe. You are glad to be up in the fresh air and sunlight again, but sorry to have Chris's conversation with Paul cut short. Then you have an idea.

"You know, Chris," you say, "you can't talk with Paul now, but you can read some of the letters he wrote."

"Really? Where?"

"At my house. In my Bible."

"Say, let's find AL!" Chris says.

THE END

From your hidden listening post beneath the window of the house, you soon hear several voices. Two do most of the talking. One you recognize as Judas's. The other seems to be that of an older man, and is full of scorn.

"So, Judas Iscariot," says the older voice, "you offer us your help in the arrest of Jesus bar Joseph, the prophet from Galilee..I am pleased, but also surprised. Were you not a follower of his?"

"Yes, I was," Judas says crisply.

"But you choose to be no longer. Why is that?"

At the question, Judas's anger surfaces again. "Because I have seen that he is a fool! He is not what I thought he would be."

The older man gives a cluck of disapproval. "Not the king you wished him to be, eh? Well, he is too much of a king for us. We wish no trouble with the Romans, though you and your kind wish for a great deal. But no matter; we are agreed on one thing. This Jesus must be gotten rid of!"

"How much will you pay me for my services?" Judas asks.

"Thirty pieces of silver," the older man replies. You hear rustling, then the clink of coins.

"I will keep you informed of the proper time for the arrest," Judas says. Then you hear the swishing of robes. It seems the interview is over. You feel sick, for you realize what is about to happen.

"They're going to kill Jesus," you say grimly to Chris. "But I guess Jesus knows that."

"He knows it?" Chris is shocked. "And he's still going to let it happen? I'm confused. What was Jesus really up to?"

"Let's go back to Professor Q's and talk about it," you say wearily. "I don't want to stay around here; I've seen enough." Chris nods agreement.

"I do have one piece of good news," you add. "Jesus' story has a happy ending."

THE END

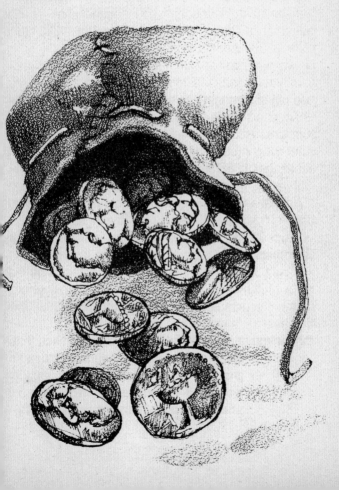

Still shaking from your encounter with the soldier, you and Chris wander around Rome for hours. You are amazed by its beauty. Everywhere the buildings are of white marble with stately columns across the front and carved figures above the columns. Every street corner seems to have a fountain or a statue decorating it.

After a while, though, you begin to tire. You'd heard that Rome was built on seven hills, and now you know it's true. All this walking up and down hills makes you think of the vacation your family took to San Francisco. Unfortunately there are no cable cars to ride in Rome.

You and Chris sit on the edge of the next fountain you encounter, dipping your hands in the cool water, splashing it on your hot faces, and looking up at the charging marble horses carved in the center of the fountain.

You are wondering what to do next when you hear a familiar voice say, "Greetings, brothers."

"Lucullus!" You'd never expected to see any of your friends from the catacombs again.

"I'm so glad to see you. We were worried about you when you didn't return. I knew you'd met a Roman soldier. What happened?"

Choices: **You tell Lucullus the truth, that you denied being a Christian (turn to page 143).**
You tell a tale that makes you sound brave (turn to page 147).

"Well, as a matter of fact . . ." It's not easy, but you manage to tell Lucullus about Claudius, and the fact that you denied being a Christian.

To your surprise, Lucullus is very understanding. "It's not easy to tell of your allegiance to Christ when you think your life may be at stake," he says. "Did you know that one of the apostles, Peter, once lied about Christ three times — because he was afraid?"

"Tell us about it," Chris says.

"Well, Jesus had been arrested by the Temple police and taken to the High Priest. Peter followed to see what would happen. But as he sat, a servant girl accused him of being one of Jesus' followers. He denied it completely! When other people asked him, he lied two more times. He even cursed Jesus in the process."

You wince a little. It sounds awful. Yet you know it could happen so easily.

"The sad thing," Lucullus continues, "is that Jesus had just said that Peter would deny him three times before the cock crowed in the morning. So when the cock crowed, Peter remembered it all. He ran away weeping."

"Wow. Pretty heavy," Chris comments.

"But Jesus forgave Peter," Lucullus adds quickly. "He forgives all of us for the ways we've rejected him — if we ask. But I won't take time to explain that now. I'm still going to see Paul in prison. Why don't you come with me?"

Turn to page 149.

You don't think much about which button to push. The machine vibrates for such a long time that you doze off.

When you awake and climb out of the machine, all you see around you is a swampy woodland. The ground is covered with luxuriant, lacy ferns, and underneath them it is squishy and damp. Huge trees tower·above you.

You hear the soft, swishing sound of water, the scratchy noises of insects, and the flutter and chirp of birds in the trees. But with all this, the earth seems strangely quiet, as if it were holding its breath, listening.

You and Chris don't speak. You don't want to disturb this strange peace.

Suddenly a deep, throaty roar tears through the trees, ruffling their leaves like a wind. Then you hear the crashing of giant feet. You dash madly for the machine, but it's too late. The creature is blocking your way.

It stands twenty feet tall on its clawed hind feet. Its tail swishes heavily over the ground behind it. At the top of the monstrous body, the great head sways. Wide nostrils sniff at the smell of fresh meat. The huge mouth yawns like a dreadful red cave rimmed with teeth, each about six inches long.

Tyrannosaurus Rex!

THE END

146

You arrive back at the Professor's laboratory. He asks you if you want to go back in time again.

Choices: You say, "Sure!" Now you can choose where to go next: Egypt (page 32), Jericho (page 40), Jerusalem (page 51), Rome (page 33), or Mount Gilead (page 92).

You say, "No, thanks. I've had enough for now." Now you can choose to put your bookmark here until later, or just plain start over on another day.

"Well, the soldier took us in custody," you explain to Lucullus, "and he wanted us to deny being Christians. He said he'd let us live if we cursed Christ. Of course, we wouldn't do that."

Chris looks at you strangely, but says nothing. You take a deep breath and stand up on the edge of the fountain to continue your tale.

"So we told the soldier that we were Christians, and he started hauling us off to prison. Right away I began looking for an opportunity to escape. And it came! A runaway chariot was thundering down the street, and the soldier shoved us aside to—" Suddenly, as you gesture to explain your story, you lose your balance.

"Look out for the marble—" Chris yells as you fall backwards. You hit your head on something hard, and then everything goes black.

Turn to page 154.

Without looking back, you dash across the room and out the front door, letting it bang shut behind you. The scent of the professor's roses, the warmth of the sun, and the sight of two kids riding their bikes down the street are almost as much of a shock to you as the desert had been a few minutes ago.

You jam your hands into your pockets and walk slowly down the sidewalk, kicking aimlessly at the fallen leaves, until a thought turns you around abruptly. You shouldn't have left Chris alone with that crazy professor. What if something terrible happens to him?

You run back, past the rosebushes and in the door without knocking. "Chris? Hey, Chris!"

Silence.

You slowly explore the house. It seems that both Chris and the professor have disappeared.

So has the machine.

THE END

You soon find yourself with Lucullus in the center of the city. He proudly points out the sights to you. "That is the Senate House," he says, "and this open area is called the Forum. The most important men of the Empire meet here to discuss matters of importance."

You look at the men in togas who stand beneath the stately columns of the Forum to talk.

"Impressive," Chris says.

Then Lucullus turns another direction. "And this is not so impressive," he says. He points to a low, grim-looking structure.

Lucullus's voice is sad. "This is the prison where they are holding Paul," he says. "It is not a pretty place. The lower dungeon used to be a cistern."

You step back a bit. "Isn't it dangerous to go see him?"

"Perhaps," Lucullus says. "But Paul is allowed to have visitors, and it is a great comfort to him to hear news. You see, I doubt very much that he will leave this place except to be executed."

Turn to page 152.

When you find Jesus and his disciples again in the crowd, Jesus is saying something about the Son of Man suffering at the hands of his enemies. The disciples are protesting the idea.

"When Jesus says 'the Son of Man,'" you whisper to Chris, "he's talking about himself."

"You mean he's planning on dying?"

You nod.

"I don't get it," Chris says. "Jesus has all kinds of powers. Can't he protect himself?"

"I think he could, but he's decided not to."

"Why not?"

You take a deep breath. "Well, the whole human race is under a curse because we've rebelled against God. And the only way to break the curse was for God to send his Son to live on earth and die."

"Oh." Chris looks a little perplexed.

"The main thing you should realize is how much God loves us even though we don't love and obey him. Jesus is willing to give up his power and die, just to help us."

"Yeah." Chris is beginning to catch on. "I can see now why Jesus means a lot to you. When is all the terrible stuff going to happen?"

"I don't know. Want to stay and watch?"

Chris looks at the ground. "Well, you may think I'm a real ghoul, but I'm not. And in this case, it's enough for me just to know what Jesus did."

"All right," you say gently. "Let's go home."

THE END

After Lucullus speaks to the guards, you descend the stairs into the prison. The lower level, your destination, smells damp and dirty.

Seated in chains on the far side of the cell is a powerful-looking man in a tattered, dark green robe. His reddish brown hair and beard are streaked with gray and his strong features etched with deep lines, as if he's suffered a lot.

Beside him is a younger man, using a quill to write something on parchment.

"Paul's writing a letter," Lucullus whispers.

Then you hear Paul speaking: "Remember Jesus Christ, raised from the dead, descended from David. This is my gospel, for which I am suffering, even to the point of being chained like a criminal. But God's Word is not chained. Therefore I endure everything for the sake of the elect, that they too may obtain the salvation that is in Christ Jesus, with eternal glory. Here is a trustworthy saying: If we died with him, we will also live with him—"

Suddenly he looks up and sees you. "Oh, hello, Lucullus. I was just writing a letter to Timothy. I see you've come to visit me, and you've brought friends."

"That's right, Paul." Lucullus introduces you. Then he and Paul chat briefly about people you don't know. You and Chris stand there silently for a while, and then Chris bursts out with a question.

"What's all this dying stuff about, anyway? I don't get it. It almost seems as if you Christians enjoy the idea of death!"

Paul and Lucullus look a bit startled at the outburst.

Choices: **You are embarrassed, and ask Paul to excuse you while you take Chris outside (turn to page 136).**
You wait to hear Paul's answer to the question (turn to page 138).

A bird is singing in the tree above you. You sit up and rub your eyes drowsily. Boy, what a great sleep! And you had a really wild dream, too, but you can't quite remember it.

The gate in your fence squeaks, and you look up.

"Hi, Chris!"

"Hi. How are you feeling? Want to go with me to Professor Quinten's ?"

"Professor who?"

Chris looks at you strangely. "Professor Q. You know him."

You shake your head. "Sorry, Chris, but I don't know what you're talking about. Why are you staring at me?"

THE END